Olly McGilloway was born in 193⟨ ⟩ on the right bank of the River F⟨ ⟩ from open countryside. He is an ⟨ ⟩ sity teacher. He also researches and presents the BBC radio programme *Nature's Way*, and for years has been a close observer of minks and other wildlife. His previous book, *Along the Faughan Side*, is a detailed account of the River Faughan – from trickle to broad mouth. He met Greyhood along the middle reaches of the Faughan.

TO MY SONS
TONY AND DESSIE

GREYHOOD
The Year of the Mink

Olly McGilloway

THE
BLACKSTAFF
PRESS
BELFAST AND WOLFEBORO, NEW HAMPSHIRE

First published in 1988 by
The Blackstaff Press Limited
3 Galway Park, Dundonald, Belfast BT16 0AN, Northern Ireland
and
27 South Main Street, Wolfeboro, New Hampshire 03894 USA
with the assistance of
The Arts Council of Northern Ireland

Printed by The Guernsey Press Limited

British Library Cataloguing in Publication Data
McGilloway, Olly
Greyhood.
I. Title
823'.914[F]

ISBN 0-85640-401-2

CONTENTS

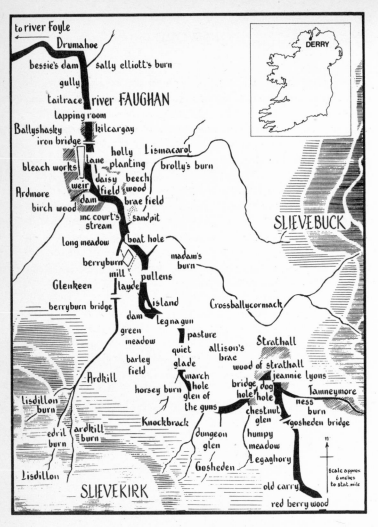

GREYHOOD'S TERRITORY

FOREWORD

ALONG THE middle reaches of the river, less than ten yards away, grey and difficult to see in the fading light, a young dog mink stood and stared at me. He was with his mother and she tried to hide him from me. She was grey-brown and beautiful, with white chin and breast drifting into grey beneath. I called her Dusk. His shoulders were noticeably grey so I called him Greyhood.

The river, called Faughan, stretches twenty-nine miles from Sawel Mountain, the highest peak of the Sperrins, to where it joins the tidal water of the River Foyle in the townland of Campsie. It starts in a stern rocky glen called the Eagle's Nest, halfway up Sawel, near Cloghornagh at the march with County Tyrone and runs north-west across the centre of County Derry.

The story confines itself to the first few miles of the Faughan's middle reaches: the territory of Greyhood.

I thank my sons Tony and Dessie for their company along the river, searching and watching; and my brother Ken, my sister-in-law Helen and Jack Gamble for bringing the story to Blackstaff Press.

Olly McGilloway
Derry, January 1988

PART ONE

DUSK

WITH SPRING barely two weeks old, it would take a fortnight before the Boat Hole pool could begin to liven again. The wren, flitting about the white willow gathering catkin-down, was carefully quiet. Even the blackbird flying from bank to opposite bank did so without a 'tchook' or a chatter. A magpie was too busy using her beak to say anything. She was laying twiglets from a nearby sycamore across a used nest in a blackthorn. A brown rat entering the water beneath the lowest knob of the sycamore, to swim fifteen yards to the left bank, was careful to be quiet. It was early evening but light was beginning to fade. It would be dark in another half-hour or so.

The day had been bright and sunny and brown trout, kelts and smolts followed nymphs to the surface and leapt after hatching flies. The frequent dimpling and occasional splashing had happened from noon till the late afternoon but now, except for the ream of the swimming rat, the surface of the pool was unbroken. The loss of heat through a clear sky had caused the fish to lie deep and the pool's surface air to condense into a fine mist. It was a still evening with only the sound of the river, called Faughan, streaming over gravel and between steadfast rocks, breaking the quiet.

As the brown rat hurried away from the Boat Hole, Dusk moved into it. The mink had come upstream and swam into the lower belly of the pool, before turning left over a shallow gravelly bed to reach a hob. This was her usual landing place from downstream. She sniffed the low bank and climbed out of the water. The hob raised her into the mist and every muscle in her dark body trembled with the cold. The water was warmer than the air. She would not dally on this low bank; the damp air was heavy with smells and she began separating them to find food. A faint smell of rat excited her and, returning to the water, she found the smell getting stronger as she nosed her way up the pool.

The rat had left the water a minute earlier, but her body-air lingered as misty particles above her crossing place. Dusk swam beyond this place and the smell grew weaker. She turned left, stretched her neck into the air, and then, pushing a figure-of-eight ream on the surface, paddled back to where the rat had crossed. In the air against the raised left bank she soon sensed more recent rat and followed the smell into a spill-over cut. Once used to take the layde's excess water, the cut was now a dry drain, five feet deep and less than two feet wide and overgrown with nettle and blackberry briar. It ran forty yards away from the river to meet an old millrace which had worked the Berryburn Mill but now it was also a dry lane.

The mill building itself, unused by any kind of miller for more than forty years, stood derelict above the family of the brown rat. She kept her young in a nest of hay over flakes of sycamore bark about ten feet inside an extravagant hole under the front entrance to the building.

Dusk took her time moving along the cut. The warm smells of fur and weeping milk were easily followed. The rat, a nursing mother, had used the cut to return to her nest. She left it about ten yards before it met the layde bed, passed behind dog rose among hawthorn and entered the hole under the front of the mill. Dusk arrived a short while later and followed her in without any difficulty.

The floor of the rat-hole sloped downwards, behind the founds, into a roomy rock-walled pit. The place was dark, warm and dry and littered with feathers, and the bones of birds, mice and fishes. It was very quiet.

Just inside the pit, Dusk stopped and stared. She watched the rat coming towards her, stayed still and purred. The rat moved very quickly to position herself between her nest and the purring fitch, and died. Raised on hunkers, scolding, with three naked blind babies clinging to her breasts, she died. A split second after Dusk had filled the air before her, the rat died instantly.

After biting into the rat's neck, Dusk scraped the sucklings onto the floor and tossed their mother towards the pit's entrance, then she moved to the nest. Five scaldies squealed, responding to her tongue with working mouths, and Dusk purred before eating them. She ate ravenously, swallowing the first whole and chewing the others. Then, after searching the rest of the pit and finding nothing of interest, she returned to the fresh sucklings. The last turned her stomach. She was overfed but licked the vomit and

4

emptied rancid dirt over the stain before dragging the sow rat out of the pit.

Twilight had gone and the grass was steeped with damp air when Dusk eased from the rat-hole. She stood still, looked around her and listened and searched the mist's smells for enemies. In front of her, beyond the hill called Slievebuck, the sky was impossible to see. Behind her right shoulder the moon looked very pale over Gosheden Hill. Downstream to her left, she heard the river moving away from the Boat Hole pool and pipistrelle bats squeaked in the air above her. She paid the bats little heed for she was using her wits to find danger. With the night friendly, she dragged the rat from the hole, lifted her by the neck and hurried along a deep trench.

Formerly a tailrace, the trench ran thirty yards from the mill to meet the Berryburn at the lower end of the Boat Hole. With the rat on the ground between her front legs, Dusk drank from the burn. She was going home but would have to swim sixty yards of quiet pool, beneath a high left bank, and tumble another hundred yards of racing water to get to her den beside McCourt's Stream in the townland called Glenkeen.

Dusk found the rat easier to carry after stepping into the river but felt the dead thing coming alive in the deeper water. As soon as she began paddling down the pool she felt the rat's tail stroking her cheek. On several occasions she felt the rat lifting over her nose and had to duck and then shake her head to prevent being smothered. Beyond the pool, racing water at the start of McCourt's Stream tried to pull the dead thing away from her and she bit into bone to keep it secure. Struggling onto a low left bank, she hurled the rat before her. She was exhausted and her jaws were sore and tired. No matter; moments later she tore the rat's face away. Thirty yards further, she climbed a sandy bank to hurry behind the remains of a tailrace grid: swept from the Berryburn years earlier. She crept into her den – a snug fur-and-feather-floored place at the end of a two-yard tunnel, where sand met clay through the roots of a mature ash tree – and pushed the faceless rat against the back wall. The night was misty and cold and Dusk was very tired. She was too sleepy to stay awake.

Dusk looked like most other wild minks. Asleep and curled up, with head resting on bushy tail, her back, shoulders and belly, were the same grey-brown as the heap of rat-fur lying behind her. The colouring of the rest of her body – dark brown with white markings on her lower face and breast – was ordinary enough and, like others of her kind, she would start shedding her thick coat within the month.

Her young were nearly ready seven weeks after early success in heat. Her partner – her third in February and best of all – had been an exciting mate: big and strong and friendly. Yet he had left to serve another and another after her and would never return to Dusk's den beside McCourt's Stream. Now curled up, she slept alone and slept soundly.

GREYHOOD IS BORN

THREE HOURS passed before Dusk uncurled herself to attend to the rat lying against the back wall. After eating the remains and licking its lining dry, she spread the pelt over her couch. She peered through the grid guarding the den, smelt the misty air, listened for any strange sounds and then moved into the night. She moved down the sandy bank to the edge of the river. She was very thirsty and spent half a minute lapping up Faughan water – before easing her whole body into it to cross to the townland of Lismacarol. Her insides were becoming lively and she would want to return home before long.

She found the current heavier against the opposite bank and let herself drift for thirty yards past alder, birch and willow onto a sloping rocky shelf. This place, across and downstream from her den, covered with damp sand, showed the prints of heron and rat. She ignored these and scrambled the bank through leaves of celandine towards a drystone wall. She chased a wood mouse through the wall into a brae-field, but the mouse ran under branchlets of beech among mint. Dusk hated mint. Its reek clung to her coat, burned her nostrils and made her sneeze. The mouse escaped. No matter; the field was sprinkled with much animal dirt and the bitch could smell rabbits all around her. She usually found food in this field, and already could see a young rabbit crouching close to the drystone wall. She climbed onto the wall and moments later killed the cub: a young buck, sick with swollen eyes and ears, who could offer only a mew-like squeal to the terrible new pain in the back of his neck. She ate a mouthful of the cub's belly, placed the remains in the opening of a disused burrow and made her way up the field.

The field sloped steeply for about two hundred yards to meet a spread of flowering gorse against a sandy bank. The gorse held fibres of sheep's wool, hid blackbirds and linnets and covered a hundred rabbit paths. The sandy bank held many burrows beneath hawthorns. The hawthorns kept finches and sparrows. A beech wood, downstream and to the right, hosted many birds and animals, including badgers. An old sandpit separated the upstream side of the field from Brolly's Burn. Moorhens, reed

buntings and frogs used the Sandpit. Apart from gorse and hawthorns the field grew a scattering of benweed and thistle, and
played host to a variety of visitors – most of them after food. Dusk
was also after food but her insides were getting livelier and she
wanted fur and wool for her nest. She knew this place and that its
gorse held much wool. She hurried up the field.

She failed to catch a hare along the upper half of the brae and
caused herself serious hurt. She was breathless during the chase
but when pains in her lower back and belly dragged all her
strength away she collapsed. She collapsed under buckled legs and
her eyes and head rolled in agony as the kits tried to leave her. She
squealed in terror and twisted her neck to snap instinctively at the
source of the pain. Then with trembling mouth, she grabbed a tiny
paw and pulled the first kit free. Four others followed the breech
to deliver themselves on the brae while their mother crawled
beneath the gorse into unconsciousness.

The mink's plight had not escaped notice. An old boar badger
watched her try to catch the hare and then lie down near the
thicket of gorse. The badger was hungry and too busy sniffing the
entrance to a rabbit stab to pay her any other attention but her
screams disturbed him. He knew many minks but had never heard
them like this. He knew them as purring fitches, bad-tempered but
always quiet, whose smell hurt his eyes like woodsmoke. The boar
started clawing into the roof of the stab and ate red worms, and
then pink worms and a blackhead worm, before causing a pregnant doe to leave her nest empty. Seconds before the stab caved in
and minutes before delivering her first cub, the doe had bolted
from the nest. Now the badger scraped through the couch of
rabbit-fur and caught another blackhead worm and three sour
green worms. He chewed the blackhead and swallowed the green
worms and then shuffled through damp benweeds to hunt slugs.
Twenty yards further he picked up the strong smell of mink and
found five kits along a trail of ice-cold slime. He gulped down the
kits and started to follow Dusk's stains to the edge of the gorse but
stopped short. The day was breaking and blackbirds were making
noises in the Beech Wood. It was time to go home. He turned
away from the stains and the smells of mink through gorse and
lumbered down a path used by badgers long before pairs of leaves

grew from mast to become the oldest trees in his great Beech Wood.

When daybreak came Dusk was seen lying in the tent-like shelter of gorse. Rabbits watched her sleeping with her back towards them. She lay on a hard bed of dry earth five feet away from the open field. The rabbits were still watching when her shoulders stirred but they ran to the burrows beneath the hawthorns when she started to move her head.

She awoke shortly after daylight hearing the voices of birds in the gorse around her, in the hawthorns behind her and in the Beech Wood. She also heard the bleats of lambs in a nearby field and mewling from beneath her. Rounding her aching neck she found a tiny pale kit in her groin. The kit, a newborn son and bare all over, was no bigger than a hazel catkin. He was warm and sticky but began trembling when she opened her legs. She lifted him into her armpit and licked his face and body clean. He was blind and hungry and a sore grief to himself. She quietened him with her first milk.

Remembering the terrible thing that hurt her in the dark, Dusk turned her head and blinked at the Brae-field but she could sense no danger, only the smells of rabbits and her own drying secretion. No matter; she was frightened, and wanted to take her sleeping kit to the den beside McCourt's Stream. She took him into her warm mouth before attempting to uncurl herself but pains in her middle back and shoulders caused her to lie still. Except for her lower belly and between her back legs, numb and swollen with pain and bruising, she hurt all over. She returned the kit to her armpit and purred and fell asleep.

She had been asleep two hours when the loud rattling of a cock blackbird startled her awake. The blackbird had been taking a short cut to his nest and started complaining when he found the way blocked with a furry stranger. He retreated noisily and flew to the highest hawthorn to scold the bitch with a string of 'tak-taks'. Dusk ignored the bird's noises for the sudden fright and movement he caused her had made the kit cry. She gave the kit a hurried look, curled up tight, and moved him from her armpit onto her bushy tail and licked him all over. After ten minutes she tried moving her back legs but only disturbed the kit again.

9

Growing very restless, she tried taking the kit into her mouth but breathed with difficulty. Her mouth was rough with thirst and her body was warmer than before. It was mid-morning but the gorse thicket would know the heat of the sun two hours before noon. Dusk could not know this but her instincts told her to move to some other place.

Soon she lay perspiring and short of breath. Her whole body felt damp and she could not bother trying to make sense of any smells; only her ears and eyes worked. She could hear the continuous singing of birds all around her, and watched the cock blackbird flying into the far corner of the thicket. The cock alighted on a thick branch of gorse above an even thicker branch supporting his nest. He had flown straight from the Beech Wood for his mate had laid her eggs. Still angry, he now seemed to be scolding his mate. The hen left the nest without a word to fly through a skylight while her quarrelsome mate covered their five new eggs.

Dusk rounded her neck to look again at the Brae-field. The ground behind her was warmer than before and spikes of warm light were coming through the ceiling of gorse. She could feel her benumbed parts starting to ache and strange tinglings in her back legs gave her the fidgets. She scraped a shallow pit in the ground beside her, lined the scrape with fur from her tail and, after nosing her sleeping kit into his new nest, rolled on to her belly.

She lay sweating and breathless and scared of the bright heat. A soft breeze across the entrance to the lie helped dry her forehead but the still air inside the thicket was suffocating. She lifted her head and shoulders but came down with a flop when she tried to raise her hindquarters. Now her hind-undersides were stinging and she burned her tongue trying to lick them better. After several attempts with failure, through weak and hurting middle back muscles, she lifted her hindquarters. She succeeded by forcing her chest and shoulders forwards and downwards. After three clumsy falls she crept outside the gorse to bathe her whole self in the soft breeze. Then she began walking between woody stems and working her way towards the far end of the thicket of gorse.

The cock blackbird felt the eggs tremble when Dusk used the nest's cross-branch to pull herself upright. A second later he heard

10

scratching and felt the eggs being pressed against him. The nest moved and he almost hurt himself on green spikes as he escaped through the gorse-top. Immediately, the whole neighbourhood heard him scolding. Dusk listened, but not before she had devoured the five new eggs. She returned to her kit and lay down beside him for she was still weak and very sore.

She awoke shortly after noon when the kit began to make his mew-like sounds. She lifted him and licked him and fed him. Again she was very hot and uncomfortable but she waited until he fell asleep before returning him to the tiny nest. Once more she crept outside the thicket to fill her chest from the light breeze and, this time, she collected wool hanging from the gorse.

A few moments after re-entering the thicket and adding to the kit's bedding, she hobbled over the dry ground, between gorse uprights, along rabbit padding. She followed the path until she neared the bank where the rabbits lived: where their heavy scents quickened her breathing and made her tongue wet. Out at the bank she saw many rabbits, mothers and cubs, nibbling at grass and clover or sitting half-asleep in the sun. When she crawled out of the gorse they ran into the Brae-field or away through brambles or into their burrows. She looked for a burrow to use for the remaining hours of daylight. She wanted an empty burrow but most of the holes showed entrance dirt and led into tunnel systems. None of them held cobwebs. At last she entered a hole much wider than herself, with a spacious vestibule and a single corridor lifting to the right. She left the bank and limped away to collect the kit.

Eight or nine lengths from the bank she saw a bird descending through the ceiling of gorse into a cup-shaped nest. She let the hen linnet settle for ten seconds or so before eating her and waited a minute before eating the four eggs. Another bird, with a grey head, reddish front and nasal voice, shouted accusations against her. She left the cock linnet twittering to himself and went back to her nest. She found the kit crying, lifted him carefully and returned to the burrow to feed him. While she settled down in the cool darkness about three feet inside the bank, a big buck rabbit came into the burrow by another entrance.

Dusk saw the broad face of the buck in the burrow's side

11

corridor. She purred and spat at the thing but he lunged at her. She twisted away from him but he kicked her back and snapped at her. When she rolled under him and tore a mouthful of fur from his chest he ran over her face and was gone. She sprang after him and then lay breathless and trembling. She turned to look at the kit and quickly took him out of the bank to find another place.

Fifty yards beyond the gorse Dusk moved through a spread of bramble and nettle at the Sandpit end of the field. Without pausing she hurried below a wire-and-post fence and half slid down a steep bank into a ditch. The ditch ran alongside the Sandpit and held grasses, rushes, and broad-leaved pondweed in a trickle of water. The pondweed's uncovered leaves and stems carried a rust-coloured scum which stained the water. Dusk was breathless and very hot. She opened a hollow in a tussock of thick sedge beside the ditch, placed the kit inside the opening and drank the brown water. A lark and a pair of reed buntings watched her from a safe distance and the scents of frogs made her hungry. She ignored these things and collected the kit, climbed out of the ditch and then started to creep through knotweed between the Sandpit and the Faughan's bank. After fifteen yards of knotweed stems she discovered a section of concrete drainpipe and went into it. This place was cool and dry and felt safe. She crept for two lengths of herself into the darkness and lay on her side. When her son was fed and still she licked her hind-undersides and fell asleep.

The kit had cried several times during the late afternoon and early evening but Dusk failed to hear him. Now he was crying again and she answered him. She awoke two hours into darkness and fed him. She was very hungry herself. Again she made him a nest with fur from her tail and left him sleeping in it.

Outside, the sky was overcast and threatening rain. She ate a long-tailed mouse before leaving the knotweed and two gravid frogs near the damp ditch, then spent awhile lapping up ditch-water and felt the first spits of rain on her way back to the pipe.

The badger from the Beech Wood had trailed Dusk's scent from the gorse thicket to the wire-and-post fence. He felt rain in the air and decided against following her into the Sandpit. He waddled along the side of the fence, and then turned right to follow the drystone wall across the bottom of the field. Approaching the

Beech Wood, he picked up the smell of a dead rabbit – the young buck killed by Dusk during the previous night. The old boar found the partially eaten cub inside the mouth of the disused burrow and tried to hurry the thing back to his sett in the wood.

Dusk paid little heed to the rain as she carried the kit through reeds, past thistles and under a goat willow. She pricked herself crawling beneath low gorse and soiled her coat jumping through mud into Brolly's Burn. Across the burn was the bank of the Boat Hole, and across the Boat Hole was the spill-over cut. She was making for the rat's pit under the mill where she had eaten the scaldies and where it was dark and dry and warm. She reached the front of the mill inside ten minutes, followed the rat-hole into the pit and put the kit in the empty nest.

The following day Dusk carried the kit across the Berryburn and swam the pool beneath the high left bank, to tumble a hundred yards of hurrying streams to her den beside McCourt's Stream. There she placed the kit on the fresh pelt over her couch and licked him all over.

He was her first and only kit and probably the first newborn mink along the Faughan in the spring of that year. He was bare and shivering and helpless and blind and unaware of any other sense, but he was safe and well, and would be called Greyhood.

THE FAUGHAN IN SPATE

THE DRIZZLE of the previous evening became heavy rain during the night pelting most of the valley until daybreak. Then it stopped all of a sudden but returned in fits and starts throughout the first half of the day. The showers stopped altogether about three hours past noon. Sawel Mountain and the other uplands had been thoroughly soaked by noon and this later rain ran down their sides. It left Sawel as spouts, with peaty freshets from a dozen burns and darker trickles from a thousand drains, to rush the Faughan to the River Foyle. By mid-afternoon the river was three feet above its normal level and continuing to rise. The surface washings, mixing themselves with sand, gave the water a yellowy brown, jaundiced look. The Faughan carried drowned sheep, branches and logs, nests of grass and other debris; it was noisy in spate and very dangerous.

The river was running heavy and broad when Dusk left Greyhood fast asleep in his new nest. Disturbed by the increasing noises and smells of flood-water, she moved quickly to look at McCourt's Stream. The stream ran faster and higher and browner than usual. It half covered its sandy left bank and scoured the right bank trying to free a low willow. Now the willow tried to hold on to a branch of beech arriving from somewhere upstream but the branch rolled and ducked away from it. More branches and things were hurrying downstream and Dusk sensed more to come. Fear moved her back to look at her son.

All the while, Greyhood lay in his bed of rat-fur unaware of the great tumbling threat outside the den. Four hours earlier his mother had safely carried him through water to this place beside McCourt's Stream. Now the water was moving up the sandy bank to drown him.

Dusk watched the Faughan rising towards the door of her home, and kept watching. She was reluctant to take Greyhood away from the den and decided to let the river come nearer. Many spates had threatened her den but always came short and then fell away. She lay on her belly, watching and waiting, and her heart beat very quickly.

14

An hour later the Faughan began to run more slowly. Beyond McCourt's, and a quarter of a mile after the pool called Deep-end Craig, the river was damming behind the bleach-green weir at Ardmore. Another half-hour found the left side of McCourt's steadying itself two feet below the waiting mink. She watched a branch as it passed her time and again – downstream then upstream then downstream – caught in an eddy a safe distance from the entrance to the den. Soon the curve of the eddy lessened and the branch bumped alongside the left bank and out of sight. Across the stream the willow was more resistant to the pull of the spate and a floating log came to rest against the right bank. The Faughan had stopped rising and, with the air light without rain, it would soon lower again. With quietening heart, Dusk returned to Greyhood and licked his blind face.

Greyhood lay in his own dark world of quiet buzzing. With open mouth, he could instinctively root at his mother when she touched his body or nest, but he could not know her or anything else outside his world. He could not know himself from anything else and he lacked togetherness. Dusk seemed to know these things and fed him and cleaned him and kept him warm, and expected nothing in return.

At twilight she went back to the den's entrance and found the spate clearing away. The heavy noise of the river had gone and McCourt's Stream was beginning to give out its own sounds again. The water had changed from yellow-brown to peaty black and foam-flecked. It was sinking down the sandy bank leaving loose branchlets and twigs, old leaves and other litter and, across the stream, the wet stems of willows held their own assortment of caught things. Interferences with the steady surface of McCourt's flow promised the appearance of the tips of the rocky bed in a short while, but now the stream continued to run angry. It was too dangerous to cross and Dusk would have to stay on her own bank to find food. She moved through the grid before the den and hurried away from the river, past the ash tree over her home and into a long meadow.

MEN HUNT THE FOX

THE LONG Meadow, a gentle decline of eighty yards, between the road which runs from Ardmore to Gosheden Bridge and the river, belonged to the lower slopes of Lisdillon Hill. A hedge of hawthorns, showing a few rowan trees, hid it from the roadway, while alders, willows, the occasional ash, young sycamores and holly trees, stopped it becoming the Faughan's left bank. The meadow stretched for about a hundred and fifty yards. It had a scrubby downstream side where a spread of gorse and willow and low hazel led into woodland. A tidy cricket pitch separated the upstream side from the Berryburn. Half a dozen cattle used the meadow and would enjoy its herbage in a few weeks' time. But now a greyback crow, two magpies and a blackbird were busying themselves in and around a hay dispenser. The dispenser, a circle of a thing with spaced iron uprights, stood ten yards from a gate into the roadway. Dusk would hunt mice through the hay during the night but she would try for other food during the last half-hour of daylight.

She stopped five yards into the meadow and searched the air. A slight upstream breeze brought the musty smell of rabbit, and a heavy smell of fox – like turnips going bad. She moved warily in the direction of the scrubby bank, and halted fifty yards from where a fox was trailing a large doe rabbit from a thicket of gorse. Dusk watched the fox, a fiery-brown dog with white face and noticeable ruffs, dragging the rabbit into the field. He held the doe's right hind leg, trailed her face into the middle of the meadow, dropped her and then raced back to the thicket. Seconds later he returned holding a cub rabbit by the neck and dumped the youngster beside the doe. He then proceeded from one rabbit to the other, tearing both of them apart in a casual manner.

The pair of magpies and the greyback flew from the hay dispenser and landed about ten yards from the fox. The magpies queried with nasal 'renks' but the fox ignored them. The arrival of another pair of magpies caused the greyback to 'kaa' three or four times at them, before flying into the woodland. A couple of young rabbits watched the scene from a short distance behind the fox and a cock pheasant walked into the meadow from the wood. The pheasant pecked at something below a broad-leaved willow behind the fox, before strolling towards the hay dispenser. All the while the fox chewed the bones and insides of the cub. Then he lifted his head and looked around him, left the cub and reached for the torn doe.

Dusk was still watching when the pheasant stepped into the hay dispenser. He reappeared after a few seconds and flew down the meadow, over the scrubby bank and into the woodland. No matter; Dusk had become excited and crept out of the meadow onto the river bank. She would run against the breeze to get closer to the fox and his spectators – especially the rabbits just behind him.

She ran over wood sorrel and anemone, past primroses and through a dense spread of bluebells; and in her haste she snapped at a slow frog. The thing squelched in her mouth and a residue of spawn dripped onto her chest. After more foul-smelling bluebells, she crawled between ash saplings into the meadow and rested in a hollow to peer at the fox.

Now and again the fox turned his head to look at the magpies grabbing mouthfuls from the cub rabbit. Then he looked at Dusk but returned to eating the doe. Half a dozen rabbits sat in a daze and Dusk eased her way behind them. When she found herself between the rabbits and the scrubby bank she galloped forwards and killed a young buck. The other rabbits scattered and the magpies lifted themselves three or four feet into the air. The fox turned and glowered at her but stayed with his doe. By the time the magpies returned to their meal, she had killed another young buck and hurried him onto the river bank before collecting the other. A few moments later she positioned herself between the two rabbits and began to claw into them.

Just as darkness was falling, and while the fox was turning to leave his rabbit, two men climbed the tubular bars of the gate from the roadway. The gate creaked and clattered causing the fox, the magpies and Dusk to look up. The men dropped into the meadow and were just past the dispenser before they saw the fox. They decided to creep alongside the scrubby bank. The fox watched them for a few moments and then left the doe and half ran past gorse into the woodland. The magpies flew after the fox and Dusk left her rabbits to peer at the men from behind a low holly bush. She watched them coming and heard their voices growing louder. One of the men held a length of wire with a looped end; a smaller man carried a piece of pointed wood about a foot long. They stopped beside the doe rabbit.

Dusk moved back to her rabbits and crouched between them. The men were still in her view and she watched them. For a while they stood motionless above the doe and Dusk heard the small man give sounds like a dog otter. He whistled for a short time. The sounds were unanswered and he began to talk quietly. 'That's a brute of a dog, and a cheeky one at that. Worth a few quid – eh?' The other man said nothing.

The sounds frightened Dusk and she kept as low as she could. Their shapes grew bigger and she thought the silent man was peering in her direction when the same voice said, 'Look, it's getting very dark. We'd better get this thing set. He ran to the right of that whin. We'll fix it to its stem.'

The noisy man had started to move towards the gorse but stopped short when the other said, 'Will you wait a minute and take a good look. We'll need to narrow the run and keep it low. We'd be better to keep it tight and fix the peg. Show us it, deepen that cut and give me a hand to crowd the thing.'

The small man started to whistle again and hacked a slit in the top of the tiller, before following the other man across the scrubby bank. They collected branchlets of willow and hazel from behind the bank and used them to narrow the run past the thicket of gorse. They also used a thick heavy branch as a crossbar to make the fox crouch through the run. The tall man forced two inches of the tiller into the ground, then positioned the noose-end of the baling wire across the run and held it in position by slotting the wire's stem into the tiller's slit. He fixed the free end of the snare to a thick stem of gorse and said, 'That should do the trick.' The other agreed and then started whistling again.

A short while later Dusk watched the men strolling up the meadow towards the roadway and waited to hear the sounds of the gate before moving herself. Soon she carried the biggest of her two rabbits to the entrance of the den and was about to go back for the other when she heard Greyhood crying. She hurried into the den, pulling the rabbit behind her, but the kit was safe and she would feed him before long. She placed the rabbit against the back wall of the den and quickly left. She paused to drink Faughan water and to empty herself before re-entering the den with the other buck rabbit. Then she licked and fed Greyhood and, when he was fast asleep, she returned to the Long Meadow.

The moon was pale beyond Gosheden Hill and the stars of early April looked far distant when Dusk moved into the meadow. The night was cloudless and the light breeze had become more westerly. The breeze carried a moist chill from behind Lisdillon Hill, and a few bird-smells but little else of any interest. The louder-than-usual sounds from McCourt's Stream drowned the busy squeaks of pipistrelle bats, but all else was much as usual.

Dusk ran across the meadow to where the fox had left the doe rabbit but it had gone. She sniffed about the place and picked up the salty sour smells of men and then followed the smell of fox tainted with rabbit. She passed ash saplings and climbed on to the river bank towards the edge of the woodland, but she was unsure of this place and returned to the meadow. There she skirted the scrubby bank and then moved in the direction of the hay dispenser. Shortly she caught three long-tailed field mice and she ate them all. She moved out of the dispenser and stopped to pick strands of hay from her chest and belly. Then she hurried off to the cricket-pitch side of the meadow.

Again pipistrelles were flitting about the sky but a large moth-shaped thing, drifting across from the old mill, caused Dusk to hide beneath a hawthorn tree. Almost instantly the owl hissed and swooped overhead to reach the dispenser in the top right corner of the meadow. Dusk ran as fast as she could. Many times she had seen the white owl flapping from the sky to attack ground things. She ran down the meadow and through the grid before the den and stayed there.

The barn owl continued to hunt the meadow and then flew upstream to her nest on a ledge in the mill.

When daylight was beginning, Dusk crept out of the den and fixed her eyes upon every flying thing above the Long Meadow. Wood pigeons, blackbirds and other early risers were flying about the place but the owl had gone. She ran to the edge of McCourt's

Stream and drank and washed herself in the shallows. The Faughan was its normal level again and a golden amber colour.

For the following three days and nights Dusk hunted the Braefield and the Sandpit on the other side of the river. She did not return to the Long Meadow until the late evening of the fourth day and there she saw the fox again.

The fox, entering the meadow earlier that same evening, had crouched through the run past the small thicket of gorse to grab a young buck rabbit. He knew this run but found it more crowded than usual. Branchlets and other tree rubble were making the run tunnel-like and caused him to squeeze his way through to reach the cub. He eased into the gap, crept the length of himself and then rushed at the rabbit. The next moment there was a deep burning in his throat and felt himself becoming dizzy. He was about two feet into the meadow before the snare had dug into his upper windpipe and prevented him going any further.

The cub rabbit heard the fox's hoarse sounds, ran to the mouth of a burrow and stood and watched the fox strangling himself.

The fox felt blood oozing from the sides of his neck as he tried to move forwards. Instinctively he retreated and then moved forwards, retreated again and then rushed forwards, shaking the gorse bush. He writhed in agony and became shocked and frightened when his spittle collected and his voice went and stayed quiet and his tongue refused to move. With his strength spent and his insides heaving from him, he collapsed backwards into a sitting position and died.

Others had joined the cub rabbit to watch the fox becoming still and harmless and then they went about their usual business.

At sunset Dusk crossed the Long Meadow to search its scrubby bank. She had picked up the smell of fox and would be careful. Twenty yards short of the bank she saw the fox looking at her from the thicket of gorse. She recognised him as the fiery-brown dog who had killed the rabbits four sunsets before, and she stopped in her tracks to see what he would do. Birds were singing and flitting about the bushes beside the fox and rabbits were sitting a yard or two from him. Dusk waited for him to pounce into the meadow but he stayed where he was. She relaxed and crept towards the scrubby bank.

Sometimes the fox seemed to move and Dusk could feel her back-hair tightening, but she sensed from his odd stance that he might not attempt to harm her. Closer, she paused again and then moved uneasily towards him. All the while the fox stared at her, nose pointing, teeth bared and tongue lolling. She looked more closely at him and listened for his sounds but his stained shoulders and grey chest stayed still and silent. Black flies walked across his tongue to cling to mucous crusting on his lower lip. His eyes showed big black pupils and his left fang was broken. She could just about see the burnt-toast colour of the hairs behind his ears and could smell the white dirt beneath his tail. She unstiffened and then ignored him to search the scrubby bank.

As she was leaving the bank to hunt the upper end of the meadow for mice, the gate from the roadway clattered under the weight of two men. She left the place and ran all the way home, and she found Greyhood crying.

BROC THE SPANIEL

T HE RAIN returned that night to keep Dusk indoors and all
the while, Greyhood continued to lie in his dark world of
private sounds and beginning confusion. He was without
the company of brothers and sisters but his mother was very
attentive. She noticed that he was gaining size and was beginning
to grow a thin silvery coat of fine hairs. He used to open his mouth
every time she touched him but now he seemed to be less hungry.
She felt him pushing his paws against her and the edges of his bed.
He could sense her presence when she entered the den and would
stop moving until she lay down beside him. He was beginning to
separate himself from the outside world.

The next day the sun was shining. It was mid-April and, of a
sudden, catkins burst and elms became fluffy. All the shrubs and
trees – except the oak and the ash – were leafy, and the banks,
hedgerows and meadows showed their own spreads of colour.
Butterflies, bees and hoverflies visited the blooms; birds and small
mammals took up family duties; and kelts and smolts journeyed
to the Foyle. It was the time when minks started shedding their
winter coats. The valley of the Faughan would soon be popular
again; and Dusk and Greyhood would not go without much
adventure.

For the next fortnight Dusk hunted and robbed, always without mercy, and sometimes ate until she was sick. She tore the
black head off a reed bunting and devoured a moorhen in the
Sandpit; terrorised rabbits at the top of the Brae-field and about
the scrubby bank of the Long Meadow; savaged a she-stoat in the
mill upstream of the Berryburn and ate a kelt sea trout stranded at
the tail of the Boat Hole pool.

Greyhood no longer fretted so much during Dusk's absences.
When he was on his own he would become absorbed in himself.
His movements were becoming integrated and he could bring his
paws together and rub his chest and belly, and feel the tiny
whiskers about his face. More and more he would roll on to his
back and wave his legs in the air. He appeared to enjoy feeling
nothing, searching space, but became excited or more active than

usual when he touched a fresh pelt. Dusk would only allow him to lie on his back for a minute or so – she preferred him to lie on his chest. With strengthening neck and shoulder muscles, he soon learned to face forward.

That fortnight also brought Dusk moments of dread, especially when she visited strange places. One evening she had followed a cock pheasant into the woodland beyond the Long Meadow, and had been confronted by an unruly springer spaniel. She had been nosing among horsetail and the like, when she heard 'karrk-karrk' coming from the wood. She knew these sounds and wanted their careless owner, and she crept between the stems of a stunted hazel to enter the wood. It was mid-evening and the place was cool and shady and heavy with food-smells.

Following rabbit padding through bracken, she found a pheasant's tail feather: a long brown quill showing dark bands. The feather had escaped trampling and lay across the mulch of beech. Its root held a tiny column of clotted blood. Dusk sniffed the ground and air for more pheasant but the bird's smells had gone. She followed the same track for another fifty yards but she would have to go further. All the while she listened for the pheasant to say something but he kept silent.

She continued along the track and climbed down a steep bank into a fern-clad gully. The next moment she heard the voices of men and saw a man and two boys examining the cock pheasant. She heard a dog barking and saw the thing looking at her. Her heart pounded. Immediately, she turned to clamber up the bank but failed. She had to run ninety yards and thole a trail of hurts to surround herself with bramble. Dusk lay there peering through the tangle and shook with fear.

The man had seen the mink but he was not especially interested in her. Grabbing hold of the dog, he was more concerned about what to do with the cock pheasant. The boys wanted to take the bird home. 'But it's torn apart!' exclaimed their father. 'Broc's far too rough. He shouldn't be snapping and biting at a bird. His mouth's far too rough.'

Broc, nine months old, wagged his tail when he heard his name mentioned. He had accidentally disturbed the bird an hour earlier and managed to catch him. But then, despite the repeated orders 'Fetch it! Fetch it boy!' from three masters, he had started to eat the pheasant.

The man spoke again. 'We should wrap this bird in briar and let him try snapping at it. That'll teach him, that'll soon give him a soft mouth!' Then he looked at the boys and Broc, smiled at them and added, 'But sure he's still young – he'll soon learn.'

The boys nodded and proudly patted the dog, and Broc licked their hands and faces. The man softened and told his sons that they could take the pheasant home, and they moved on. But Broc, set free to follow them, hurried off in the opposite direction.

All the while, Dusk had heard the voices and watched and listened for the dog. Now she saw him coming and stared at him until her eyes hurt. He stopped now and again to sniff at tussocks but soon hurried on in her direction. She listened for his voice but he kept quiet. Behind him, the man and the boys shouted and whistled but the dog ignored them.

Dusk felt her hair tightening and her body stiffening. She was very frightened and moved herself to ease her chest. She could hardly breathe and her heart beat very quickly. A moment later the dog stopped and she could feel his warm breath, smell his woody smell and see hazel-brown eyes shining through the briar. His ears and tongue were very long and he made wheezing sounds. Now he bared his teeth and the wheezes became snarls, and then dreadful barking noises. The very next moment he plunged into the bramble and the wheezes, snarls and barks became louder. The plant's trailers jagged his face and legs and snagged his long coat, but he continued to struggle into the bush.

Dusk lay motionless, gathering extra energies in her buttocks and thighs, and waited for Broc's face. All her fear had gone. She would spring at the face and tear the thing.

Broc's big face pushed through but, reaching out from a halter of thorny stems, it was harmless. His closing eyelids impaired his vision and the plant held him like a choke chain. Now he yelped and whimpered and rolled and twisted his body, as hands tried to drag him free.

Seizing her chance, Dusk leapt forward and ripped Broc's left ear. At her greatest speed she darted past his legs and out of the briar, past his rescuers, to follow her own line back to the Long

Meadow. Half an hour later she lay beside Greyhood and re-
moved thorns of blackberry from her flattening coat, and licked
herself better.

During the ninth day of May Greyhood flickered his eyes – the
blue of sapphire – and squinted at his mother. He had left his
world of darkness.

OTTERS IN McCOURT'S

WITH THE coming of light into his own world, and much wonderment, Greyhood's eyes brought new light into the den. With circles of brilliant blue controlling shining pupils, he soon learned his mother's face and to watch his paws touching her nose and whiskers and ears. When he tugged at her whiskers, and she pretended to bite him, he would push his paws into her mouth and then lick and smell them and bite them himself. He liked to peep round his mother to blink at the entrance. When he saw daylight he sneezed and suffered the snuffles for minutes afterwards. Yet he mewled and kicked and tried to bite her, when Dusk blocked his view. She preferred him to gaze at the twilight when his eyes could stay wide open. The full light of May was far too bright.

Dusk left the den and fixed her eyes on the sky and buds of ash and other things that shone blue, or black, or blue-and-black in the evening light: bluebells and violets close to the ground; an empty cartridge fired from a shotgun; bluetits in the willows overlooking McCourt's Stream; a piece of nylon rope reaching into the stream from a low alder; a kingfisher speeding from the Deep-end Craig to the Boat Hole; the kingfisher again – flying from the Boat Hole. Still she could not find the likes of Greyhood's eyes. If she were to catch a close glimpse of him, only the alulae of the shy jay could compare with his eyes. But Greyhood would be kept hidden from all these things and only allowed darkness and then fading light, until his eyes would strengthen.

Elsewhere outside the den and along the valley grasses, buttercups and daisies and all the other plants attracted nectar feeding, pollen gathering, bark and leaf eating, and debris-collecting organisms. Many of these organisms were attracting other feeders. And these feeders, in their turn, were attracting others. In one week's time the season would begin for men to catch the Faughan's fresh-run salmon and trout, while others would hunt families of mink. For the present Greyhood had nothing to live on but Dusk's milk and she had to leave him to find food for herself.

Soon the day darkened and Greyhood watched it. He had stirred himself awake to find his mother gone and he watched for her return. He saw the day turning grey and became impatient. He was very hungry and bad-tempered, and his hunger made him alert. He watched small flickering things at the door and tried to crawl towards them. One of them fluttered close to his face and then lifted itself up and over his head. Greyhood rolled on to his back and his eyes followed the thing bouncing across the ceiling, and he tried to reach for it. When the moth jerked its way out of the den he cried after it. Then he lay frightened as sharp pains in his belly moved foul gas into his mouth. He was very hungry and he fretted and cried.

During her outing Dusk had searched the Sandpit and ate a newt and four unhatched larks. When twilight was nearly spent she crossed McCourt's Stream to feed Greyhood and there she stopped to sniff at a platform of rock. The rock, two-thirds uncovered and about four feet from the sandy left bank, showed the tarry dirt of an otter. The musky dirt was freshly-moist, yet well formed, and held fish scales and tiny bones. She knew the ways of otters and that they would not harm her: they would not harm any of their cousins – they preferred to eat fishes and birds. No matter; when she noticed webbed prints where an otter had walked her bank she quickly left the stream to follow the stranger's spoor through nettles and then ran back to search about the entrance to her den. Satisfied that the otter had not approached, she returned to the stained rock; then she heard Greyhood's cries and hurried up the bank.

The otter had watched Dusk from the far bank and waited for her to go away. He was a large dog with a very broad head and dark brown eyes. He had watched the mink from behind a low alder and saw her examining his dirt and following his smell to where he had returned to the river. He had no interest in this nervous fitch, but the stream kept hundreds of young trout. He had already eaten five smolts and would take more before leaving this place. He waited for Dusk to creep through the grid and then he dived into the stream.

Greyhood's whinging turned to mewls of excitement when Dusk appeared. And when she lay on her left side, his mewls

27

became wails. He pushed his mouth at her and tried to swallow milk with sobs, and choked. He attempted twenty gulps in half as many seconds and choked and spilt everything he got. Then he began to feed slowly, keeping the milk, until he fell asleep.

When Dusk moved out of the den the sky was clear and showing high stars. She was very sore and wanted to bathe in the stream but the place was alive with strangers and too well lit. On the platform of rock a bitch otter sat licking her paws. Further downstream a big dog otter waited for passing smolts which were tailing their way out of the stream, over shallows into a long watery glade before the Deep-end Craig.

Dusk crept down the bank and crouched behind a clump of docks. She sensed the company of other onlookers. She could smell rats in the nettles upstream of her and then saw the face of a badger watching through alders on the far bank. The bitch otter turned her head to look downstream then she slid into the water.

Fishing for fun, the dog shook a trout dead and then dropped the thing. Dusk lifted her head to watch the badger lumbering away towards his Beech Wood and, almost at the same time, she saw the whiskered face of the bitch otter returning to the left side of the stream. She crouched again and watched the otter carrying, cross-wise in her mouth, a silvery smolt onto the rock. Before re-entering the stream, the otter dropped the fish – open-eyed but without any body – to float between the rock and Dusk's sandy bank. She was very hungry but ignored the fish and hurried back up the bank to hunt the Long Meadow.

An hour before daybreak the otters returned to their cubs in the place called Leg na gun and, as dawn was breaking, Dusk returned to Greyhood. Soon after, a sow rat left the nettles to take the fish-head.

Greyhood lay face down, a yard from the couch – he had crawled out of his bed and felt something cold and wet under his left shoulder. Now in the morning light he was sniffing at a grey slug. He looked sideways at his mother and gave her a hurried mewl but went back to examining his slug. Dusk sat on hunkers and watched. She pawed at a sooty black beetle roving near Greyhood. The coach-horse, an inch-long slender thing, with fierce jaws and a segmented body, moved under the kit and tickled

28

his right side. Greyhood turned his head to look at the thing and twisted to grab it but the beetle ran away from him and, with buckled abdomen, pushed itself headfirst under rat pelts. Greyhood mewled but went back to sniffing and then licking the slug. He hated its taste and struck at it, screamed with rage and cried with hunger.

Dusk lay on her side to feed him. Again Greyhood was impatient and gulped and was difficult to satisfy. She had to feed him nine times that day and still he was hungry and could settle only for short periods.

After sunset, exhausted and sore, she left him in a restless sleep. She eased herself down the bank to enjoy McCourt's Stream and then, remembering the otters, she stopped suddenly to search the air. For half a minute she stood there and used the downstream breeze. There were no stars that night for the breeze carried heavy clouds. She could smell and hear rats but not otters. She moved into the stream and was washing herself when the dog otter lifted his head out of the water and looked at her. He was holding a smolt and the thing was writhing itself to death across his teeth. She stumbled backwards onto the dry sandy bed, shook herself and glowered and hissed at him. He ignored her rage and opened his mouth, yawn-like, to let the fish drop into the water. Instantly he clamped on to it again, crunched the thing's head and, lurching forwards, he climbed onto his favourite rock.

Dusk kept hissing at him and he seemed to shake his head at her – accidentally releasing the crushed fish. Any other onlooker would have thought he threw the trout at her, for it landed between her front feet with its tail in the water.

She stood her ground and tried to threaten the dog but ran up the bank when the shape of another otter loomed in McCourt's. The bitch otter squealed and jumped out of the stream to butt the dog and then swam into the shadows of the far bank. The dog followed his bitch and Dusk soon heard them splashing about the tail of the stream and saw them running across bare gravel. They were playing and would not harm her. Still, she was frightened and lay beside the grid in a couch of plantain. A sow rat, swollen with young, moved from the nettles towards the dead fish. Dusk killed her as she was reaching for the smolt, and took her time carrying the rat back to the den.

Inside she found Greyhood retching and screaming with hunger. His middle was rigid and jagging chest pains, with stabs lower down, made him roll in agony. Dusk placed the rat against the back wall and then fed him. She waited nearly ten minutes for him to fall asleep, and another minute passed before she reached for the rat. She ripped open the rat's undersides and ate six of the unborn young and then she fell asleep herself.

Two hours later Greyhood started crying again, and again Dusk tried to soothe him. But before attempting to feed him herself, she sucked in some of the rat's organ pulp and lifted a tiny foetus out of the rat to keep Greyhood occupied. He ate the thing quickly and fell fast asleep.

During the following week Greyhood ate other unborn rats – as well as the flesh of fish, birds and skinned frogs. He also ate a violet ground beetle and woodlice, and millipedes and centipedes, and he stopped suckling.

TWO FISHERMEN

DURING THAT same week in mid-May the sooty buds of the ash tree were unfolding into crinkly finger-shaped leaves. And in the wood, at the downstream end of the Long Meadow and along the right bank of the Deep-end Craig, the oaks were beginning to leaf. All the Faughan's trees were awake again and the meadows and braes were busy. The hay dispenser stood redundant in the Long Meadow and sheep were using the Brae-field. Birds' nests were everywhere and the bushes and trees offered steady jingles from chaffinches, robins and tits. Dippers, kingfishers, grey wagtails and herons busied themselves close to the river bed. Rabbits were all about the place and there were clear signs of badger, fox, otter and rat. And while the mix of black-thorn, bluebell, mint and damp grass scented the air, anemone, dog violet, forget-me-not and primrose coloured the banks and attracted much insect life.

Inside the den Greyhood had learned to stand and walk, and his darkening coat had become a smoky grey. His eyes now matched the colour of his coat. The weaning was sharpening his senses and developing his chest and rump. He enjoyed exploring the den's tiny nooks and crannies and disturbing any kind of crawling thing – ground beetle, woodlouse, millipede, worm and slug. He killed almost anything that dared to rove or crawl without his prompting. He would not eat slugs. He played biting-games with his mother, and sitting inside the entrance to the den awaiting her return had become a habit with him.

The same day he stopped suckling his mother had led him down the bank to take his first drink from McCourt's Stream. At sunset, when weanling minks leave their dens, Dusk led Greyhood through the grid and rushed him into a clump of browned ferns. Then she stood and looked around her and listened, and smelt the air for danger. With the air friendly and soft, she relaxed and allowed Greyhood to leave the bracken. While he was looking all about him, she hid herself in his hiding place. Panic swept through him when he realised she had gone. He searched the air for her smell and rushed to the ferns, and there he found her. Again she hid herself, this time in a different clump of ferns, and again he found her. She used two other hidy-holes, but he found her each time. She crept down the bank and crouched behind docks. Grey-hood watched her for a moment and then galloped after her, fell into the docks and, at the same time, tried to catch an orange-tip butterfly. She pawed him to be still and made him lie on his belly, without fidgeting, until it was time to move. Then she led him across the dry sandy bed and both of them drank from the stream.

Dusk slid into the shallows and turned to look at Greyhood who watched from the bank. He made no move to follow her. She hurried back to him and together they drank a little more. Once again she went into the stream but waited this time for Greyhood to join her. He slowly moved towards her, feeling the water cover his body, the trapped air in his fur keeping him afloat. All the while Dusk watched him closely. Soon he was using his partly webbed feet to walk through the water without touching anything else. Now he was swimming.

Over the stream midges moved like clouds of smoke and swallows and swifts swooped to take them. And out of dull quivering duns in the banks' herbage came spinners: bright shiny flies with amber, or claret-brown, or yellow bodies, ready to mate and die. Already spent males were falling to their death and females were landing on the stream to lay their eggs and die. Their shiny bodies – with upright transparent wings, fragile legs and whisker-like tails – could be seen all about the surface of the stream. Near the deeper right side of McCourt's, beyond the current, brown trout were inconspicuously feasting.

For nearly ten minutes Greyhood and his mother swam in the shallows and Dusk was very careful to prevent him moving towards the current in the centre of the stream. She felt unsafe in shallow water without cover of any kind and moved onto the sandy bank, shook herself, and waited for Greyhood to do the same. He was tired and his legs could hardly carry him. He lay down before reaching Dusk but when she slipped into a hidy-hole he scrambled up the bank to find her. Back in the den he yawned and tried hard to keep his eyes open. His mother gave him a piece of rabbit's shoulder and he enjoyed it, licked his paws, and yawning, he fell fast asleep.

That week also brought rain and, with a reasonable flood, the smolts and kelts found their way to the Foyle, while fresh, mature sea trout and salmon entered the Faughan's tidal reaches. The trout smolts, born less than three years before in the small gravel of the Faughan's side-streams, would stay near the mouth of the river for the next few months and even return as pickers for a brief spell, before moving into the Atlantic. Next year these smolts would return as mature trout. Well-mended kelts would try to make their way back to the river within a few months. The salmon smolts, however, born in the bed of the Faughan itself, would leave for the very deep Atlantic without delay to eat its herring, eels and krill. They would attempt to come back in two or three years. The fresh and mature sea trout and salmon, already in the tidal and brackish waters, were waiting to reach the Faughan's freshwater streams and pools. A month or so, with another flood, would welcome these past-smolts through McCourt's Stream.

Anglers had once been permitted to search the river's tidal and lower reaches from the first day of April through the remaining spring, before following the sea trout and salmon the whole summer and beginning autumn until the twentieth day of October. This threatened the smolts' and kelts' spring passage to the sea, greatly endangering the natural cycle of the fishes. But now they were protected: permitted angling could not start before the twentieth day of May – after they had left the river.

It was two days after Greyhood's first trip to the stream that the fishermen came. The smolts and kelts had gone and the big sea trout and salmon were back but confined to the tidal reaches until more water allowed them to move upstream. Tidal anglers tried to catch them. Freshwater anglers waited for them and, in the meanwhile, fished streams like McCourt's and pools like Ardkill Dam and Deep-end Craig for brown trout.

Dusk turned to leave the den to hunt but, just as she was getting ready to step through the grid, she smelt danger. Instantly she dropped on to her belly, positioned herself to peer through the grid and lay motionless. Two men – fly-fishers, tall and quiet like their cane rods – were standing beside the nettles at the edge of McCourt's watching the water. Dusk settled down to peer at them.

As they moved away from the bed of nettles they talked quietly to one another and, all the while, they kept looking across the stream, watching the brown trout sucking in the spinners. One turned his body to look behind him and Dusk felt her neck-hair rising, but he did not look near her. He looked at the ash tree above the den, at the hawthorns on both sides of the tree and at the dense cluster of blackberry briar along the left upstream bank. The bramble was hanging over the bed of nettles. His gaze returned to the ash tree. Dusk heard his voice, 'It's all a bit crowded. . .' He turned to the stream again and pointed at the otters' rock. The other man looked about him but said nothing.

Both men were concerned about the space between the low sandy bank and the heavy foliage behind them, and the rocky bed of McCourt's, which was too treacherous to use. They could have fished the new sea trout and salmon in the crowded tidal pools but they preferred being with the brown trout in their lonely places. They would take a salmon or a sea trout if either happened their way but a brownie was what they were after. So they would have to keep low to get near the trout feasting themselves beneath the far bank's alders, but the ash tree, the hawthorns and the heavy bramble would not allow this.

Dusk grew less tense. She sensed that these men were not concerned with her or Greyhood – that they would not harm her. Still, she lay and looked on.

One of the men flicked at the midges and mumbled to his companion as he crossed the shallows at the tail of the stream. He disappeared behind a spread of willows on the right bank to try his luck further downstream. Dusk watched as the solitary fisherman stooped to gather little claret and yellow spinners from the stream. He searched his fly-box for anything that looked like the spinners. He found only claret and yellow spiders but these were tail-less wet flies. No matter; he would try them on the surface. He coated his nylon leader with bees' wax to keep it afloat, attached the flies to it and moved to the edge of the stream.

The trout were taking close to the far bank, under the alders. Conscious of the bushes behind him, the fisherman cast his line across and upstream. The line and the leader, and after them the flies, fell crooked. Disgusted with his cast, he was about to retrieve the flies when the line tightened and the rod-tip buckled. A trout had hooked itself. The yellow dropper fly had presented without disturbing the water, and had moved into a slow circular drift to trail the flow of the stream. It had moved and behaved like a spinner and the nearest trout had reached for it. The fish felt the jag of the hook and tried to swim away from the thing. An instant later it leapt out of the water and fell, lopsided, back into it.

During the leap, the fisherman had lowered the tip of the rod to prevent the hook being torn out or the line being snapped. Now he let the trout run but kept it under his control. When it had tired he raised the point of the rod to keep the brownie's head out of the water, and when it began to drift he drew the fish over the net. He was pleased and said something to himself.

He was kneeling on the sandy bank examining the trout when the other man returned. Both of the men admired the fish: a firm three-quarter-pounder in beautiful condition with a golden brown back and showing black and reddish spots along its sides. Darkness came suddenly and its owner carried the fish to the edge of the stream, immersed it in the shallows to get rid of surface grit and blood, and then put it into his fishing bag. Dusk watched as the two men left McCourt's bank to make their way back to the Ardkill Dam and, when they were out of sight, she crept through the grid and ran over the roof of the den into the Long Meadow.

She returned an hour later with a large doe rabbit from a burrow in the upper end of the scrubby bank. The rabbit looked healthy enough but she had been easy prey – made slow by a tiny painful swelling between her hind legs. Despite this early sign of myxomatosis, Dusk and Greyhood would enjoy the taste of her, and she was large enough to keep them well fed for two full days. A quarter-pound of the doe's flesh would give the bitch a good single meal. Greyhood preferred the liver, kidneys and the like, but would refuse the gall bladder.

When Dusk moved through the den to pile the rabbit against the back wall, Greyhood felt the ground trembling beneath him. He lifted his face and his tiny eyes watched the faint light being blocked out as the bitch came towards him. His sharp muzzle knew her and the smell of fresh rabbit made his mouth water. He played biting when his mother passed him to reach the back wall.

Later, when Dusk and Greyhood crept out of the den, they saw a rat crossing the dry sandy bed in the direction of the bed of nettles. From where Greyhood stood the rat looked like one of his ground beetles and he wanted to catch the thing. He became restless but his mother pawed him to be still. Now the rat stopped to nose the place where the fishermen had knelt to admire their brown trout and, of a sudden, but with the stealthiest of movements, Dusk slipped down the bank. And Greyhood, sensing the importance of the occasion, tried to move like her.

Greyhood was ten feet away, but close enough to see the kill, when his mother bit into the rat's neck. By the time he joined her, Dusk had dropped the rat between her front paws and was examining it. She looked at Greyhood and backed away from the still rat. He sniffed at the thing, then backed away from it himself, and looked at his mother. She grabbed the rat by the tail and dragged the dead thing alive. And Greyhood pounced and bit into the rat's face – he was learning.

GREYHOOD'S FIRST KILL

I N THE late evenings that ended May, Greyhood played at
killing things. He trailed Dusk and watched her every move. He
watched her looking, listening, smelling and then following
the line of food. She was thorough, sure-footed and very careful
not to be seen by her quarry. He watched her creeping towards
her prey, pouncing upon it from behind and biting into the
animal's neck. Then she would wait for Greyhood to attack the
dead thing.

He had played the same game over and over, and he always
looked forward to the biting part. At first he waited for the animal
to move before he would attack it and Dusk would have to push
or pull the dead thing before he would react. Only when his
neck-hair raised, heart pounded, chest tightened and legs trembled, would Greyhood attack and bite into the thing to make these
feelings go away. Soon they were triggered by just seeing the dead
thing and he would attack the animal where it lay. He would bite
into its face or neck or back. But then Dusk would position the
victim's head under her chest so that Greyhood could only bite
into the thing's back or the back of its neck. Eventually he came to
prefer biting into the back of the stranger's neck.

All the while he was learning to stalk and hide and creep. He
noticed that the scents of rabbit, bird, rat and mouse – outside the
den – were less similar than their dead smells and he liked the taste
of their warm blood.

It was during the first gloaming of June that Greyhood made his
first kill.

That evening, as Greyhood and Dusk were leaving the den,
heeding the smells and sounds of the outside air, they heard the
loud screaming of swifts and looked up at the noisy bird-things
speeding above McCourt's Stream. Then they saw the flash of
another bigger bird crossing the stream from a gap in the far
bank's crowd of alders. The stranger, glinting grey-blue and
reddish, lifted himself above the line of racing birds and, without
any change of pace, flipped upside down to take one of them from
beneath, completing a spiral to return through the gap in the

alders with his victim. Save for the sounds of his few wing-beats, the sparrowhawk had kept quiet.

While the hawk had been flying in the direction of the left bank, Greyhood felt Dusk pawing him to be still. But by the time he was still the bird had gone to be with his mate, who was building their nest in Gosheden's Dungeon Glen.

After the attack the swifts relaxed, chasing and racing, swooping and wheeling above the stream, but one of them crouched on the sandy left bank. She had been flying upstream when the hawk arrowed across and then upwards from the stream's left side, narrowly avoiding his line by a sudden shift – to the right and downwards. The movement had caused her to glance off the surface of the stream onto the left bank. Now she crouched on the dry sand, about three yards from the stream and the same distance from Greyhood. She was unhurt. But her short legs, embedded in soft sand where the bank levelled to reach the stream, had kept her aground. She sat alone.

The minks saw her and, from where they stood, she looked like a dark brown stain on the sand. She sat facing them with forked tail and scythe-like wings reaching towards the stream. To Greyhood she seemed a jagged shape and a tantalising moving thing. He watched her trying to disappear when she showed her white breast, and reappearing when she lowered her head again.

Greyhood followed Dusk down the bank and the swift saw them coming – like dark silent clouds. Then the clouds were moving above her and she lowered her head as if to let them pass over. And now they were behind her. When the swift raised her head again, Greyhood crunched her skull and left the body for his mother.

The following evening, while Greyhood and Dusk were sitting outside the den, a young doe rat crossed the sandy bank. The rat was about two and a half months old and would be able to breed in a fortnight's time. Greyhood saw the rat and wanted the thing. His heart pounded and his legs trembled. He looked at his mother. He expected her to kill the thing but Dusk refused to move.

When the rat was nearly at the place where the swift had been killed, she stopped and sat on hunkers. Greyhood watched her sniffing the air and listening, and then staring in his direction. He

38

could not know that the breeze coming from the hill called Slieve-kirk was carrying his scent across the sandy bank. Again he looked at his mother but she stayed still. He looked at the rat again and could feel his back-hair and chest tightening, and when the thing started to move towards the nettle-bed, he left Dusk and crept down the bank. He crept among bracken and grasses with soft feathery flowers but he was far too slow and clumsy. The rat smelt and heard him, and saw him, and ran away from him. And Greyhood followed Dusk into the Long Meadow.

THE LITTLE FAT MAN

A T FOUR o'clock in the afternoon of the ninth day of June, as Greyhood and Dusk were sleeping in their den, three men walked the right bank of McCourt's Stream. They were walking towards the Sandpit. The tallest of them carried an empty cage: a rectangular frame with iron walls and handle. The smallest of the three – a little fat man – carried a supermarket shopping bag which held the offal of a couple of rabbits. The third man carried a well-used ferret bag: a green canvas purse of a thing with a wooden base showing air-holes. Two of the men were experienced mink trappers. The little fat man with the bag of offal was there to kill the trapped minks.

The cage was a trap. It was twenty-four inches long, eight inches high and eight inches wide. It had a strong wire door which could only open inwards. A metal flange, like a lower lip, prevented it from opening outwards. Inside the cage, hinged on to the floor, six inches from the back wall, a flat plate of metal ran from side wall to side wall. The metal plate which reached two inches high – tilting towards the back wall – could only be moved inwards and downwards. Two stout iron wires, each about seven and a half inches long, attached to the underside of the metal plate, lay along the floor of the cage. These lengths of wire were designed to hold the opened door against the ceiling of the cage: that is, until the metal plate was pressed downwards, and the wire props were pulled inwards, causing the door to snap shut. A length of strong nylon cord was attached to the front floor of the cage. The free end of the cord would be used to fasten the cage to some kind of fixture.

The bait, in this case offal, would be tied to the floor of the cage with a piece of fine wire. It would be set well away from the walls of the cage and beyond the trigger mechanism: the metal plate. To reach the meat, then, a mink would trap itself by entering the cage, walking on and pressing down the metal plate which snapped the door shut.

The ferret bag was used to carry any caught minks. It already held a dead male: a young dog taken from a trap in the place called the Holly Planting. The mink had been drowned in its cage an hour ago. Since then the trappers had inspected another trap in the Beech Wood, but that cage was empty and they just replaced its bait with fresher stuff. Now they were going to place a trap in the Sandpit.

Two of the men were doing a lot of talking. The little fat man was asking many questions and the tall one with the cage was trying his best to answer him. A week earlier the fat man had blamed minks for killing twenty-three of his chickens and a bantam rooster, and vowed that he would kill twenty times twenty-three minks.

The third man, who held the mink in the ferret bag, said nothing. He just listened and looked around him and stopped to light a cigarette. He looked across the stream, saw the grid and leaned back against the drystone wall which separated the right bank of McCourt's Stream from the Brae-field. He saw the dark hole behind the grid: it looked like the kind of place that minks would use. After lighting his cigarette he followed the other men upstream along the bank.

Later that evening when told about the likely den beside McCourt's Stream, the little fat man became both angry and excited. Angry because he had not been told earlier and excited by thoughts of returning to the place. If there was any chance that the grid had minks behind it, he would return to kill them, and he would kill them himself.

And all the while Greyhood and Dusk lay asleep.

SOLDIER RATS

THAT NIGHT the sky was starless and promised a million drops of rain, and the air made low whistling sounds. Grey clouds followed by others, black with rain, driven across Slievekirk by a strong westerly, made the sky very dark. An hour after midnight the rain started and spread the length of the Faughan valley. It hardly waited to come. It just poured out of the sky and drenched everything. It caught Greyhood and Dusk in the nearside of the Long Meadow but they were able to get to the den in a matter of seconds.

Inside, Greyhood and Dusk licked themselves dry and listened to the pebbles of rain pounding the roof. Already, tiny streams trickled down the meadow to reach McCourt's. Soon puddles would gather where the meadow flattened to meet the sandy bank.

An hour later the floor of the den, between the couch and the back wall, showed damp patches. A puddle forming beside the ash tree over the den was getting bigger and heavier and was beginning to soak through the clay, finding easier passage alongside the tree's roots. Dusk led Greyhood to the space between the couch and the entrance and pawed him to stay there. Then she moved to the grid and saw water gushing down the bank from the Long Meadow. She returned to Greyhood.

Within ten minutes water was dripping from the roots of the ash tree – where sand met clay at the back of the den. After another minute, Greyhood followed Dusk out of the den.

The sky seemed darker than ever before. But the air was silvery bright with chains of rain, bouncing and noisy near the ground. The minks ran through the puddle beside the ash tree and hurried towards the upstream end of the Long Meadow. They tried to find shelter beneath a dense hawthorn but its tiny leaves only showered them with large drips. They made their way into the cricket pitch and again failed to find any shelter. Then Dusk remembered the rat-pit under the mill beyond the Berryburn. Greyhood splashed behind her, across the cricket pitch, towards the burn.

42

When they arrived at the Berryburn it was running fast and noisy, and was too dangerous to cross. They ran along its left bank – in the direction of its source – and about eighty yards later came to the Berryburn Bridge, which joined the townlands of Glenkeen and Ardkill. Without any pause, Dusk led Greyhood into Ardkill and turned left to hurry in the direction of the mill. Soon they entered the rat-hole under the front entrance to the building and rested themselves. They were soaked and shivering and needed a warm bed.

Dusk waited until all her wits returned for the air from the pit carried rat-smells. No matter; she would kill the rats and eat them. She knew this place. It would be safe for Greyhood and herself. Behind the founds they would find the place warm and dry where they would shelter with comfort. She pawed Greyhood to follow her. But after a yard she pawed him to go carefully – for the place had greatly changed.

As the minks crept along the passage, they found its floor worn smooth and crowded with litter. They trod on the bony remains of fishes, birds and mice, and saw the faeces of many rats. The fusty air carried warm singe-like scents and strange whisperings. Dusk stopped and made Greyhood stop and be still, for she sensed great danger. Then she saw a buck rat sitting on the wall before the pit. He just sat there watching them, his eyes red with congestion. He was waiting to attack them and he stared at Greyhood. Dusk felt her back-hair rising and her stomach twisting into a tight knot. She positioned herself between Greyhood and the threat. She stood very still and watched and waited. She was not afraid of any rat but she could sense the presence of many others.

When she had visited the pit before Greyhood was born, she found only a sow rat with her young. She had enjoyed killing the thing and eating the scaldies. And when she brought her newborn kit to the pit, the place was empty. Since then a group of families had moved in. Now the pit housed half a dozen pregnant sow rats, a small army of young bucks and does, blind rats, crippled rats, old mangy rats and several dozen scaldies. And two of the young bucks had been posted to watch the entrance to the pit from atop the founds.

As soon as Dusk and Greyhood had entered the pit, one of the bucks left the wall. He jumped into the pit and ran among the colony, issuing short squeaks and low whistles and making chirruping noises. Immediately, sows went to shush their scaldies and young bucks and does gave low whistles and ushered the old and crippled into far corners. Now, behind the wall, eleven young soldier rats were ready to defend their colony. The lone sentinel would signal the attack.

Still Dusk watched the buck rat. For a full minute she had watched and waited to see what he would do, but Greyhood had become fidgety. And now, squeezing past his mother, he saw the rat and tried to go for him. Dusk turned sidewards and stopped him. Then quite suddenly, at the very moment of distraction, the buck rat gave a loud sharp squeak. And as Dusk and Greyhood stared at him, he twisted his head upwards and let out one long squeal. Instantly, the minks heard other squeaks and whistles and squeals. Then only squeals that gathered and grew into a great ongoing din. Terrified, Dusk and Greyhood moved backwards and, at that moment, the buck rat leapt from the wall. He landed on Greyhood's chest and tried to bite into the kit's throat. Greyhood nearly fell backwards but Dusk bit into the buck's neck and shook him onto the floor, then she pushed Greyhood towards the entrance and turned to see other rats appearing on the wall. She saw them running along the wall to make room for others and jumping from the wall to make room for more. And now the first five or six of them were rushing headlong towards herself and Greyhood.

Soon the floor of the passage held eleven fierce rats – all of them impatient to kill the fitches. Squeals like the shrill tones of bagpipes continued from behind the wall but the attacking rats offered only the sounds of their breathing and body movements, and the air stank with their body smells. They pushed and tried to climb over each other, to dart and bite and tug at the minks' feet and legs and underparts. Other rats jumped from the crowd to savage and cling, and attempt to bring the intruders down. Because of their fear of tripping and being eaten alive, the minks could only stand and stoop, chop and defend themselves.

Greyhood stood facing the rats. He stood with his tail only a few feet from the entrance hole and his body almost filled the height and width of the place. He felt very tired but the touch of Faughan air kept him alert. The confined space protected his back and sides from many cruel teeth. But he had to contend with the leg-biting rats and those attacking his belly and chest, throat and face. He had suffered more than a score of bites but snapped and chopped, and fought like a grown-up. When a rat tried to squeeze between his hind legs, to attack him from behind, he backed out of the rat-hole to spin himself into the Faughan air. There he flung himself into a clump of bracken to enjoy the pouring rain, while two rats ran back to kill Dusk.

All along Dusk had continued to resist attack from all sides but her wits and strength could not hold out much longer. She had been less fortunate than Greyhood for her place was roomy enough to let the rats attack every inch of her. She writhed and twisted and tried to back through them. She snapped at their backs and crushed their ribs, chopped at their necks and bit into their heads. Yet they kept coming. One buck clung to her throat. She had killed him twenty seconds earlier, rupturing his belly and chest, but the buck hung there. Then another, impatient to taste her throat, tore the dead buck free and fell beneath him. When he jumped at her throat again, Dusk caught his head in her mouth and squeezed his foul air and cheek muscles and eyeballs down her throat; then she threw his twitching remains among his fellows and backed towards the entrance. She forced her body round to face the night and stumbled forwards. As she went up the passage, snapping all the way, the lowering roof and narrowing walls guarded her back and sides. Outside the hole a young buck dropped from her belly to scurry back to his low pit. She had suffered many bites but had killed five rats and maimed others. Now she looked for Greyhood and found him in a hidy-hole. Exhausted, she dropped into the bracken to lie beside him and to bathe herself in rain.

They lay there together for a short while and watched the thinning clouds moving towards the hill called Slievebuck. Now and again Greyhood held out his tongue to taste the rain and sometimes he spat back at it. When the rain died away, he began to hear and see new things in the coming daylight.

He watched a wood pigeon flapping itself out of a tall hawthorn beside the mill. Showing a broad white wing-band, the pigeon dashed noisily towards a disused meadow beside the pool called Leg na gun. He noticed a buff-tailed bumble touching his bracken and saw the bee busying herself in a clump of blackberry briar. Already some of the bramble's chubby-cheeked buds were beginning to release pink-tipped petals but the bumble would have to search elsewhere to pack her pollen basket. A skylark flighting upwards and saying 'chirrup' took his attention and almost at the same time he turned his head to see a beautiful bright plumage speeding down the air of the Boat Hole. The kingfisher piped 'chee' at him. Now he heard a bird singing, long and loud and clear from the high sky, but could not know that this was the skylark who just a few seconds before had lifted away from him. He tried to reach for a wall-brown butterfly bouncing on the air inches above him and narrowly missed a greenbottle. It bulleted off through the taller ferns.

All about him, Greyhood heard a great number of sounds and songs. He could not know who said or sang these things. He saw a blackbird with an orange bill and heard an anxious 'tchook' at the same time. Also, coal tits seemed to call 'tsu-i' while bluetits scolded him with 'tsee-tsee-tsee'. He watched a tiny russet-brown thing, with an upright tail, approaching him from the doorway of the mill. When the wren saw him, Greyhood heard the bird-thing 'ticking' and whirring past to reach low cover at the edge of the river. Sparrows and finches offered different chirps and twitters but there were too many of these birds and their sounds to know who said what. He saw half a dozen starlings and knew it was they who rattled and whistled but he could not make any sense of sounds like 'kraah' and 'caw' and 'chak' and 'chak-chak-chak' from different crows.

Then a magpie, all black-and-white except for a glossy green tail, flew close to see if the minks were alive or dead. And Dusk scrambled out of the ferns and waited for Greyhood to do the same. They felt more tired than before and their bruises and raw tears made them very sore. No matter; they would thole these hurts until they could lick them better in their den beside McCourt's Stream. They hobbled towards the Berryburn.

Half an hour earlier the Faughan had started rising. Now the

Boat Hole was running brown, gathering speed in its middle, and beginning to roar. Dusk knew this sound and hurried Greyhood downstream along the bank: she wanted to take him home. She found the Berryburn waiting to run into the swollen tail of the Boat Hole. Soon the burn's water, brown and washing over its banks with floating leaves and sticks and the rubbish of humans, would move away with the river – for now the Faughan's lift was spreading sidewards. Before long it would swirl fast and heavy, and scour and suck the banks clean. Later, when the spate would go away, the same banks would hold new debris.

Dusk looked downstream in the direction of her den, and kept wanting to take Greyhood there. But when the memory of McCourt's in spate and water coming into the den crossed her mind, she wanted to find a safer place to use. Confused and tired, she stood beside Greyhood and watched the beginning flood.

FOR FISH AND FISHERS

USK AND Greyhood stood and watched the Faughan growing into an angry mad-like thing – roaring and tearing and
bending, and lifting and throwing anything that got in its
way. An old tree bumped past, closely followed by bits and pieces
of debris. The fallen oak, showing new branchlets shooting at
right angles from its trunk, had been swept from the island of the
Ardkill Dam. The debris, much of which had come away with the
tree, would overtake the great lumbering thing before it reached
McCourt's. Now sheep and moorfowl fledglings, and branches,
and closed bottles and more branches, and leaves and many other
floating and suspended things, in a million froths, rushed with the
Faughan to the tide.

All bubbles of air, the first of these froths would run through
the gills of waiting sea trout and salmon, and they would want
more. Soon the returning trout and salmon would run the length
of the Faughan, from tidal to freshwater, and through many
streams and pools, to reach the beds where they were born; and
fishers would be waiting all the way.

The river was splashing near the watching minks and covering
its low banks. Soon it would rush into the den beside McCourt's
Stream and meet the puddle at the bottom of the Long Meadow. It
was becoming a powerful flood and every part of the Faughan's
bed – except its bedrock, embedded stumps, and heaviest
boulders – would be shifted. Even fallen trees, steadfast in many
spates, would be taken down the valley like blades of grass.

And still Dusk and Greyhood stood and watched their river in
spate. Then they moved from the Boat Hole's left bank to find a
place to sleep through the day, soon walking along the old millrace from the Ardkill Dam.

Just over a furlong beyond the mill, they passed a floodgate all
rotting and rusty. For half a century the gate had stood at the left
corner of the Ardkill weir directing Faughan water to power the
wheels at the Berryburn Mill but it had not been used in the last
fifty years. Now the floodgate was lodged in the layde bed,
leaning against a drystone wall, idle and ignored, a short distance

from where it once stood important and upright. Normally dry, except for its lip, the mouth of the layde held six inches of flood-water.

They came to a ruined weir over which the Faughan thundered. An island of sand, gravel and clay holding many grasses, wild flowers, scrubby trees, flowering weeds and a strong holly bush, would normally have been seen slanting across the river from the far bank. The island had gathered and grown when a tear happened in the left side of the weir about forty years earlier. But now there was no island to be seen for the river was running over its old course – island and all.

Growing more tired all the while, Dusk and Greyhood passed a freshwater spring at the place called Pedlars's Well. The spring had once given its drinking water to workers from the Berryburn Mill. But now with the Faughan in spate, the well was nowhere to be seen.

The minks left this place and went into a disused green meadow which stretched upstream from the Ardkill Dam and alongside Leg na gun. And there they found an old rabbit stab. Running about two yards from its cobwebbed entrance, the burrow was dark and dry. After a brief inspection they settled on a scattering of rabbit-fur at the stab's end. The fur was soft and returned their own heat. They were sore and hungry but most of all they were tired. For a while they licked their bruises and tears and then fell into a deep sleep. And as they slept sea trout and salmon were becoming restless. About eight miles downriver, the returned fishes were getting ready to leave the Faughan's tidal stretch.

Since mid-May the trout and salmon had drifted with the Faughan's brackish pools, eager to reach fresh water. No longer hungry for food, they wanted their own spawning fords miles upstream. After rushing home from the Atlantic, avoiding seals, porpoises, the nets of fishermen and other dangers, to taste mountain water and use its fresh bubbles of air, they had had to be content with the exhausted stretch of river through the townland called Campsie. Many times they felt their river moving forwards and then backwards with the tidal movements of the Foyle. And many times they themselves drifted forwards and backwards – over thin mud and past boulders and old wooden posts, and tree stumps made green with the slimes of algae. Often they saw fishermen peering at them through Polaroid glasses from the highest banks and, now and again, they were enticed by the lures of the fishers. Mostly, however, they would let fluke and eels take the anglers' bait and watch roach and pike reach for artificial flies.

Always, this tidal stretch was unpleasant. Sometimes – especially during warm sunny days – algae would continuously leave the bed of the river, float to the surface and turn the water into soup. During these times, when thick-lipped mullet were pleased to keep their mouths open, the trout and salmon would choke and have to tail away into the Foyle. For the most part they would just dally with the tide. But then in the early morning of the tenth day of June the Faughan moved of its own accord and the trout and salmon felt its first thrust. With sides tingling and gills smarting into numbness, they felt their exhausted river growing strong again.

By mid-morning the Faughan had become powerful and turbid, and the trout and salmon lodged behind steadfasts in an attempt to avoid its forces and thick tastes; and all the while they used bladders of air to keep their bodies suspended above – or below – any likely cause of hurt. By early afternoon, before the tide had turned to buffer the river's thrust, most of the Faughan's thick tastes and other irritations had ebbed to taint the Foyle. Now, the sea trout and salmon moved upstream, away from Campsie into the freshwater reaches, where the water became more and more pleasant. By early evening the first of them were leaping and climbing the weir of Ardmore's Bleach-green Dam to run the Deep-end Craig and then the length of McCourt's Stream. With the beginning shadows of gloaming, the first of the sea trout ran through the Boat Hole. And the full darkness of night brought a steady run of trout and salmon through the Ardkill Dam to Leg na gun.

Many new fishes had passed when Dusk and Greyhood awoke in a strange den a safe distance from the Faughan's left bank, halfway between the Ardkill's ruined weir and Leg na gun. They uncurled and stretched themselves. They were stiff and sore and hungry. Most of all they were hungry – they were starving with hunger.

50

ABOUT LEG NA GUN

GREYHOOD FOLLOWED his mother out of the stab to stand and search the night. Apart from the odd light in the sky, it was very dark and the moving air promised rain. Clouds had gathered over Slievekirk and a westerly breeze was bringing packs of them across the valley towards Brolly's Burn and Slievebuck. Some were a blackish colour and kept the moon and most of the stars out of sight. For the minks, the breeze prevented the usual kinds of awareness of things about the river bank, but sounds came from Leg na gun. Dusk noted these sounds for they belonged to otters. In a while she would let Greyhood see his big cousins but before then she would find food.

Overhead a few pipistrelles still searched the low sky with high shrieks and almost instantly felt new rebounds near the ground and swooped, firing more calls, to learn about the minks. Greyhood and Dusk paid the bats little heed and, when they started moving away from the stab, the bats lost interest in them too.

Soon Dusk found three or four different rabbit lines leading towards a dense hedgerow of gorse and thorn bushes beneath a spread of elderly beech trees at the upper end of the meadow. But rather than take Greyhood along the padding, she led him by the side of a near ditch – with streaming water – creeping across the breeze to get to the warren unnoticed. They arrived at a spread of gorse, close to the hedgerow, and startled a young vixen who was standing with her back towards them. She had been stooping over a dead hedgehog, eating through his soft undersides. But the sudden and unexpected sounds behind her caused her to flee without even rounding her neck. She had found the hedgehog – a mature boar who was searching the leaf litter beneath the beeches – and hurt her mouth trying to kill him. She half carried, half rolled the curled thing into the streaming ditch. For ten yards she followed his plight until he found his feet on a narrow ledge of rock above a tiny waterfall. When he uncurled himself to paddle the few inches to the bank, she grabbed his bare belly, shook him dead and carried him back to the upper side of the meadow. Then she had ripped his belly apart.

Now the vixen stood a hundred yards away from the minks, peering in their direction, still not knowing who had crept up behind her. But when Greyhood was swallowing mouthfuls of the hedgehog's sour meat she left the place.

After helping to eat the hedgehog empty, Dusk crept between stems of gorse towards the hedge. Greyhood followed her. Then, side by side, the two of them moved between two bushes of hawthorn to walk below the beech trees behind the hedge. They stopped and sat facing a screen of hawthorn, and could smell many rabbits. Greyhood felt his mouth watering his chin and chest. He wanted to hunt but Dusk pawed him to be still for she sensed the presence of bird-food. And she had picked up the scent of fox. The air held more rabbit-smell than anything else but the smell of bird was also there – strong and freshly warm. The smell of fox was weak and fading. No matter; Dusk would wait and search the air for another while. Then Greyhood sensed the presence of the bird and became even more excited than before. And when he began to slither towards the hedge the bitch held him by the scruff. He turned to snap at her but she nipped him to behave himself. When the scent of the fox had almost gone Dusk led Greyhood to the right, and then back through the hedge to where the smells of feathers close to flesh were thickening the air.

On the meadow side of the hedge, on leaf litter inside a clump of bracken, beneath runners of bramble, a large brown bird kept her glossy eggs warm. The hen pheasant and her olive-brown eggs nestled in a scrape lined with the dead fronds of buckler-fern and the fallen leaves of beech. Six weeks before, she had had nine newly-hatched nestlings showing paired brown stripes through yellowish-buff and rufous down. But stoats had devoured them. Now she had eleven new eggs and she was protecting every one of them.

So brown was the pheasant, like the mulch all about her, and so still below the breeze, that she had not been perceived even by the wits of a she-fox. The pheasant had clearly seen the vixen running across the meadow, only yards away, and she expected the thing to return. Now she kept her body still, only occasionally turning her head to one side for a moment and then to the other. All the time she kept her head low and listened for danger. She turned her head to look at strange rustlings and saw two dark blurs. Almost instantly the blurs sharpened into pointed muzzles with opening mouths and gleaming teeth. At that moment the pheasant died.

The pheasant's head and body were almost separated and the minks stood and watched the bird jerking and thrashing about in the nest. Greyhood looked at the bird's eye because, while all of her other parts seemed to be trying to escape, her head just hung there staring at him in a defiant manner. He attacked the eye and took the whole head with it. And yet, even without her head, the pheasant continued to move. While Greyhood stared at the pheasant in wonderment, his mother pushed the bird into bracken. And then they drank the eleven unformed embryos.

When the headless pheasant, still at last, was stored in the stab-cum-den, Dusk took Greyhood to see his big cousins where the tail of Leg na gun ran into the throat of the Ardkill Dam. The Faughan's flood-water had fined down to a porter colour and was sinking rapidly but, even yet, it was five feet above its normal level.

On the upstream bank a young dog otter looked at the river. A bitch otter, swimming with great power against the current, invited the cub to join her. But he stayed on the bank and licked his left shoulder. When his mother swung away from him the cub looked up again to watch her carryings-on. In the flood-water salmon and sea trout were swerving past his mother but she could only pretend to catch them. All the same, the bitch otter seemed to be enjoying herself and made several fishes jump through the air to vanish in breaking water.

Shortly, two other cub otters appeared – from the bank upriver – and engaged the lone cub in rough-and-tumble play. The cubs – two brothers and a sister – ignored their mother and enjoyed each other.

By the edge of Leg na gun Greyhood watched the otter cubs and his heart was beating quickly. They looked big and strong, with magnificient tails and broad, whiskered faces. Happy and care-free, they looked at him with friendly eyes. Then of a sudden, the cubs were alarmed by the coming of another. Across the westerly breeze, with silent wings, floated the barn owl of the Berryburn Mill. The bitch otter left the water and hurried her cubs away to their holt in the left side of the upper throat of Leg na gun. And the bitch mink hurried Greyhood to their stab-cum-den, sixty yards away in the Green Meadow.

The owl saw the fitches running to their different holes and screeched at them. Then, after circling the meadow, she lifted the dead hedgehog and found the thing empty.

At beginning daylight, when the Faughan was three feet deeper than usual but still sinking, rain poured from dark clouds. By noontime the river was big again and, with many freshening showers, would stay more than two feet above its normal level for five days. By the first day of another week the river held sea trout and salmon all the way from Campsie to beyond Leg na gun.

That week, after the seventeenth day of June, was the week of the June Fair – an occasion of the past but still in the minds of local anglers. It was the time when large schools of fishes always ran the Faughan. Every other day brought some rain, but the river moved more slowly and fishermen walked the banks to try their luck with brandling and black-headed worms, and waded lowering streams to cast Blue Charms, Fiery Browns, Faughan Purples, Peter Ross's and other beautiful flies of feather, silk and tinsel. Down the river the anglers went, past the island of the Ardkill Dam, alongside the three deep pools called the Pullens, towards the Boat Hole and McCourt's Stream, and they caught many hundreds of sea trout and dozens of salmon. On Midsummer Day the Faughan returned to its normal level.

While the anglers fished, Greyhood and Dusk had continued to hunt the Green Meadow. One night they killed seven long-tailed field mice in and about the hedges but for most of the time they hunted the rabbits at the top of the meadow – and had killed over a score of them in less than half as many nights. But all the while they missed their own home.

On midsummer evening after the Faughan had dropped, Greyhood and Dusk waited for the sun to go down. It was the year's longest evening, and as the sun set the minks left the Green Meadow to return to their own home beside McCourt's Stream. They passed the mill and then crossed the Berryburn. Soon they crept through the grid into the den. They did not remain there long for the entrance had been greatly damaged.

Dusk expected the den to be damp, even soggy, after being

flooded. She had seen the effects of flood-water in other den-like places and had been reluctant to return with Greyhood before it had dried. Now, while they were creeping through the grid, both minks seemed excited and pleased to be there. But Dusk became greatly agitated when she saw the state of the place: immediately inside the grid, cold light and air pierced the ceiling and similar ruptures were found along the den's length. Also, small piles of fresh sand covered the floor as far as the den proper.

One week before, at eight o'clock in the evening, after the heavy flood had settled, a man had walked McCourt's left bank with an iron bar in one hand and a mink cage in the other. The little fat man hated minks and was determined to kill any he would find. He was thoroughly convinced that minks had slaughtered and eaten twenty-three of his chickens, and a bantam rooster. Since then he had killed one mink. Very soon, he thought, he would destroy a whole family of the things.

As he approached the den, he took his time. He stood and looked at the grid and then searched the bank for other holes. He checked for a tunnel system with possible exits to block with heavy stones but found none. The iron bar – a four-foot-long crowbar without any beak – he placed upon the roof of the den. The mink cage – set, baitless, with opened door – he placed against the grid and pegged it to the ground. The hole behind the grid was about four inches wider than the cage. With a heavy stone, as big as an otter's head, he blocked the gap. He stepped up onto the roof of the den, grasped the crowbar with both hands and pointing it downwards, he stabbed into the ground and penetrated the den's roof. Then he waited for minks to bolt. Nothing had happened. Many times he had punctured the den's roof, but when at nine o'clock the cage was still empty, he had collected his belongings and went home.

Now, after revisiting their den beside McCourt's Stream, Dusk and Greyhood hurried away from home again, down the bank towards the nettle-bed to return to the stab-cum-den in the Green Meadow beside Leg na gun.

THE HERON

URING THE first evening of July, when his mother was
teaching him to catch stone loaches, Greyhood felt himself
filling with fright. He saw a strange bird drifting towards
him from the sun and felt its threat, and ran to hide among the
drooping leaves of a willow tree. Dusk looked at the sky and
shared his fear. She knew the shape of the grey heron and its long
mouth and throat terrified her. Many times she had seen this bird,
all still and solitary, suddenly thrust its yellow jaws to seize frogs
and fishes; mice and pygmy shrews; buck rats and doe rats; young
moorhens and even cub rabbits. This bird was a great catcher and
killer, for many times she had seen the caught things being gulped
down the bird's long throat. Dusk felt her back-hair rising and
followed Greyhood into the willow tree.

The willow hung over a low rocky bank, about eight yards
downstream of the Pedlars' Well, and offered concealment and
some protection from the sinking sun. The sun was golden red and
half-sunk behind Slievekirk. A slight breeze across the hill caused
loose clouds to fluff into various forms and the sun gave some a
golden tinge and turned the translucent edges of others into
crimson. Now all alone in the air between Slievekirk and the River
Faughan, the heron looked a black and menacing thing in the
glowing sky.

Still the minks lay there, behind a screen of willow, with chins
and chests on dark green moss which softened a rock of grey
granite. They lay with bellies on warm sand and watched as the
dark shape grew larger.

The bird, a male heron, was arriving from a small heronry in the
uppermost branches of a mixed wood, in the place called Gransha
on the right bank of the River Foyle. As the hungry heron flies, the
Ardkill Dam was about five miles from the Foyle; the distance was
nearly twice that far for trout and salmon running the Faughan's
course.

Nearer and nearer came the heron, moving with slow and
ponderous flaps, with head tucked between shoulders and long
legs trailing. The slight breeze had helped him forward and over

the Faughan. But now, a hundred feet above the watching minks, the bird backwatered with huge vanes to a kind of hover. Then with legs lowered, the heron glided across Leg na gun and swooped down to the right to follow the Faughan's flow. Larger and more threatening grew the great bird, and the minks trembled and made smells of fear. The heron gently lowered himself onto the dam's island and then walked, with very long and deliberate steps, towards the run between the island and the minks.

Greyhood shivered and felt his neck and back tightening, and made ready to run. But Dusk pawed him to be still for the heron had stopped. And now, with scrawny neck stretched upright without a kink, and pointing his yellow bill downstream at the Pullens, the bird seemed to be listening. The minks lay very still and very quiet, and waited for the thing to go away. But the bird would not move. For over four minutes he kept his smoke-grey body motionless on lanky legs, which were difficult to see because of a rise of sandy bank. His white neck and face stayed still all the while. The minks continued to peer from their hidy-hole and saw only the heron's black crest and chest plumes stirred by the breeze, moving in relief from the stillness of the rest of him. Yet, unbeknownst to the minks, the bird's left eyelid was blinking at them and, with the retiring day, his yellow eye was turning black to get a clearer view of them. He had spotted the fitches as he walked along the island and he had kept a steady eye on them since. This island, the result of a ruined weir, was one of his favourite hunting places and his crop was empty: he was very hungry. He wanted the fitches to leave him alone and would stand still for another while. But the heron saw two fishermen walking towards him from the lower end of the Pullens. He flung open his great arms to gather air and, with long legs flexed to force himself upwards, he left the dam's island to sweep to the right over the townland called Crossballycormack. And the minks watched as he swooped down to land somewhere between the throat of Leg na gun and an angry pool called the March Hole.

By the time the two fishermen arrived to entice the dam's sea trout the grey heron had caught a lively half-pounder, still hosting sea lice, at the mouth of the place called Horsey Burn, where the Faughan tails from the March Hole and leaves the townland of

Knockbrack to run the Ardkill. After snipping the trout's life away with his scissor-like bill and carefully positioning the fish to follow the gape of his mandibles, the heron squeezed the fresh food into his empty crop. He caught another half-pound sea trout, a sizeable brownie and a score of beetles of different kinds. Then with crop nearly full and daylight almost gone, he lifted himself from the bed of the Faughan and flapped in the direction of the heronry.

Greyhood and his mother were enjoying a new-found freedom and had gone to search the hedge at the upper end of the Green Meadow. After having to lie as still as rocks under the low willow, frightened when the heron came near and petrified when he stood still and silent, the minks were very active and felt very hungry. But all manner of fearful experiences apart, that beginning night was most pleasant and useful for any living thing. The breeze was hardly noticeable and reasonable banks of cloud protected the darkness and allowed the air to keep most of its heat. Yet the sky was without any threat of rain for the clouds seemed near the stars in the heavens. It was a good night for hunting-minks and a perfect night for any competent fly-fisherman.

Between the lights, when the west is crimson and the north gleaming in the July sky, night fly-fishers begin to present their lures – crawling with bristles, darting with silvery flashes, wriggling and pulsating with interrupted and different shades of colour: Teal, Blue and Silver; Peter Ross; Butcher; Black Pennell; Watson's Fancy; Wingless Wickham; Faughan Purple; Connemara Black and many others. Sometimes the flies are presented to float on or just under the surface. Other times the flies are well sunk. Mostly the flies are larger than their daytime relations but the size will depend on things such as the temperature, colour, depth and flow of the water – and of course the moods of trout. Always, anglers like a broken sky: not too dark, never too bright. Both fly-fisher and trout shun moonlight. Banks of cloud are welcomed but rain, or the threat of it, can spoil good fishing. A short lively shower will often make dour trout active, but a drizzle can cause lively trout to go dour. Night anglers prefer air with a little movement and a hint of warmth. Both fisher and trout resent condensation: when cold air takes heat from the water. When a

58

fine mist steals over the Faughan's surface many trout lie low and most night fly-fishers go home. Both night angler and sea trout agree in wanting the water crystal clear, or pale amber-coloured, and without much depth. Between the lights, night anglers use the shallows, for sea trout move to the throats and tails of pools. At the end of the day and during the first hour of full darkness – when salmon are more sullen than ever – sea trout can become very active and vicious. Then they will snap at flies and make geared reels screech like barn owls, but run and leap and do their utmost to escape the fly-fisher's play.

And so it was on that beginning night, when the heron and the minks left the Ardkill Dam to search elsewhere, that two fishermen arrived at the dam to catch sea trout.

By midnight – when the old day ended – the men were enjoying themselves without feeling unwanted, for the bitch otter and her three cubs had left Leg na gun more than a week before. The otters had followed the main runs of sea trout upriver and that very night they were swimming and searching the pool called Jeannie Lyons. During the first hour of full darkness, the fishermen caught thirteen trout between them. At first each used different patterns of fly but, after a while of trial and error, one particular pattern proved its superiority. Nine of the thirteen trout caught were taken on a black-hackled and black silk-bodied fly – ribbed with fine oval silver tinsel – showing a tail of red floss silk: the offspring of a nymph-like pattern called Bloody William. At two o'clock in the morning, half an hour after the sea trout went off the take, the fly-fishers put up their rods, climbed the bank to the Green Meadow and dandered downriver towards the Berryburn Bridge.

Greyhood and Dusk had searched the meadow's hedges and filled themselves with young birds from early broods. Now they stood near the middle of the meadow and watched the anglers strolling along the river bank. Looking at them, memories of the heron crossed Greyhood's mind but these two-legged hunters were not interested in his kind.

HALCYON

TWO DAYS later at the far side of the dam's island, Greyhood and Dusk witnessed a very strange happening. There they watched a grey-haired man being swallowed by a huge bird – still as the grey heron but much larger and the same colour as the island's trees and bushes. Then they saw the man again and he was alive, and they watched as he crouched close to the Faughan's shallows, splashing his face and shaking his head like a big dog otter.

The man, dressed the same colour as the tent, had stepped into his hide to test its outlook. He required a clear view of a circular hole in the river's sandy right bank. The hole, the size of the man's clenched fist, smooth-edged, seven feet above the level of the Faughan and immediately below overhanging grasses, was the entrance to a nest of kingfishers. He wanted to observe and photograph, and know the behaviour of this legendary bird. The ancient Greeks gave the kingfisher the name of Halcyon, meaning 'conceiving at sea'. They believed that the mother bird formed her eggs at sea and that the gods forbade the winds to blow during the 'halcyon days' of the kingfishers' breeding season at the winter solstice.

On the twentieth day of June a pair of adult kingfishers had made a ledge for themselves in the Faughan's sandy bank behind the island of the Ardkill Dam. First the cock, in flight, struck the bank with his bill and then the hen flew at the bank and struck the same spot – each bird loosening a piece of bank with every strike. When a ledge had been made, the kingfishers – able to work steadily and rapidly – started chipping flakes of sand from the bank to open the nest-hole. They picked deeper and deeper until a tunnel, sloping slightly upwards, was six kingfishers long. Then they excavated a spacious nest-chamber. By the last day of June six oval eggs were laid: thin-shelled and glossy white, translucent like porcelain. The eggs were laid atop the parent birds' droppings, and fish and beetle remains.

This had been the kingfishers' second attempt to rear young for on the tenth day of June, just three weeks before, the Faughan had flooded their nest in the right bank of the Boat Hole pool. On that day – two days before they were due to leave the nest – eight full-fledged chicks were drowned.

Since the twentieth day of April the grey-haired man had been observing the kingfishers of the Boat Hole. After the June floods he followed the parent birds upriver and discovered their new nest behind the dam's island.

Now, from the island, he measured the distance between the hide and the Faughan's right bank. Twice he measured the distance: almost four of his strides across a shallow stream. During his second visit to the right bank, he forced a branchlet of sycamore – without any leaves – into the river's sandy bed and fixed it there with an anklet of rocks. Then about two feet upstream of the nest-hole he fastened the branchlet's stem to the bank. The stem held four sturdy side-shoots out over the stream. The twigs were more or less the same length – about two feet long – and might be used as perches. The lowest, no more than two feet above the shallow stream, would let the birds peer for minnows and stone loaches, beetles, freshwater shrimps and the like. The highest, about two feet upstream of the hole and about six inches lower than it, might entice the returning birds to stay there awhile – for a speeding kingfisher is not easily seen, just a blur of iridescent blue with emerald green and tawny brown.

In the fading light, returning from the bank to the island, the man saw the minks and stopped to stare at the young male, and had to stare hard for the dog had no markings – just a dark greyness. And there seemed a dim kind of blur close to him like the later twilight before full darkness – like dusk.

When the man moved onto the island to get a closer look at the young dog, the minks hurried into the Faughan to cross the dam. Then they moved along the left bank, heading in the direction of Leg na gun.

After adjusting the stem of the sycamore, so that the perches would give him a chance to capture the kingfishers on film, the man went into his hide and thought about the grey mink.

THERE WERE no stars that night for a slow north-westerly lowered the sky with threatening clouds, but the clouds kept their rain. From before beginning day until daybreak, the night stayed murky and its air was far too warm for bodies in fur.

A few minutes after twelve o'clock, when the new day began, Greyhood and Dusk followed the bank of Leg na gun to bathe in the water. Soon they were splashing about in noisy shallows, like otters playing.

A quarter of a mile away, on the Faughan's right bank, a large dog mink was leaving the townland called Strathall to hunt rabbits in Crossballycormack. He moved across the bottom of Allison's Brae – where buzzards nested in a larch tree – passed the March Hole, jumped a dribbling drain and crept under a wire-and-post fence into a grassy field where sheep and rabbits lived. Frequently he hunted rabbits in this place on the outskirts of his partner's territory. The rabbits belonged to warrens at the down-stream end of the pasture and the dog mink was making for them, but he rested awhile. He would take his time for the air was heavy and too warm to dry his tongue. No matter; the night was young and the air was filled with rabbit scents. A few yards into the field he stopped and lay in a clump of bracken, and searched the air. Immediately, a strong scent of rabbit made his tongue drip. The smell was coming with the soft breeze but it was too thick to have come far. He fixed his face in the thickest air, made the rest of himself follow the line of his face and then dallied no more. Soon he found a young doe rabbit cowering in a thistle patch. When he lowered his face towards her the cub started squealing. When he snapped his teeth into her neck she went quiet.

Greyhood and Dusk had left the shallows, climbed a mossy bank and continued up the river past three hundred yards of brisk streams. Without pausing, they arrived at a quiet glade in strange territory.

The left bank held a row of early-middle-aged beech trees. The beeches, all upright, grand and healthy-looking, kept ripening barley from the river's edge. The barley, tall and spiky and the colour of gold, stretched upstream as far as the Horsey Burn, at the march with the townland called Knockbrack.

Where the downpours of mid-June had flattened some of the barley crop, and mice walked the stems to steal seeds from slender spikes, Greyhood and Dusk feasted. They ate ten field mice in as many minutes. Then they moved to the glade and there they felt wafts of their own kind of smell coming from the far bank. Dusk grew fidgety and peered at willows hanging down to the river. She had wandered too far. Greyhood sensed the agitation growing in his mother and let his eyes follow her stare across the glade.

The right bank of the glade held a spread of sallies. Behind the sallies, a pasture for sheep also hosted hundreds of rabbits, especially at its downstream end. Now deep in the midst of the trees stood a mink, motionless and with much curiosity, ready to protect the territory of his bitch. His name was Oak of Strathall.

While travelling from the thistles to hunt the warrens at the downstream end of the Pasture, Oak had heard the squeaks of frightened mice hurrying from the barley field behind the beeches. He knew the meaning of these sounds and crept into a low willow, but with the breeze across him he could only wait to listen and watch. Then he saw a bitch and a young dog mink arriving on the far bank. For a full minute he watched them staring in his direction before he left the willow to cross the glade.

Greyhood and Dusk had peered through the thickest air at the willows but failed to see any mink. But before long they saw a shadowy movement near the lowest willow and a gentle stir in the river. Again they saw nothing of any mink and Dusk became anxious and more fidgety than before. Then, in the deepest water halfway across the glade, they saw the bobbing face of the dog mink looking at them, and heard the glade slopping their bank.

Greyhood and Dusk stood their ground – they would not flee from one of their own kind. While they were purring themselves rigid and ready to meet the bold face, the big dog shook himself out of the glade and climbed the bank to challenge them. Greyhood and Dusk retreated until their sterns felt barley stems; then they waited.

The stranger-mink appeared suddenly between the trunks of

two of the beech trees and, without pausing, ran straight at Greyhood and Dusk. Dripping wet, with head thrust forward, teeth bared and tail rigid, he stopped two yards short of them. He was a fearsome sight but Greyhood tried to copy him. Now all of them stood still until Dusk dropped on to her belly with chin on ground. She had regarded the wet dog's stance, saw only warning and yielded. Bewildered by his mother's behaviour, Greyhood threw questioning glances at her. He wanted to lie beside her but something in his nature kept him standing. He stood gamely and still like the big dog mink, except for trembling legs and tail.

Oak of Strathall looked at the cub, ignored his warning, and began to creep nearer. Again he stopped, this time a yard away, with muzzle pointing at Dusk. Then, teeth covered, he looked with dark eyes at Greyhood and approached the bitch.

Almost instantly Greyhood slipped away from his mother's right side. He moved further to the right of her and then a yard towards the beeches. He was not afraid. He just wanted to be ready to attack this enemy-mink from the rear.

With his left eye Oak watched Greyhood but was more interested in the cub's mother. He reached forward with his front right paw to touch her head and with a sudden movement, the bitch half snapped at it, chopped air and then lowered her head. Expecting Greyhood to react in some way, Oak looked at him, but the cub kept still and watchful. Oak turned his gaze to the bitch. He neither purred nor showed teeth but he stood very still. For ten seconds neither moved. For a second time he reached his paw forward. And again, of a sudden, the bitch opened her jaws. But this time she kept them open – as if to yawn rather than snap – and lowered her head. Once more Oak looked at Greyhood but the cub remained watchful.

At last Dusk let the big dog touch her, and she accepted it, for his touch was friendly. She lifted her head and saw white markings on his chest and chin. Above, his eyes were like black shiny beetles and the rest of him was dark brown like very old oak leaves. Neither moved until the sounds of hurrying foot-falls turned their heads to see Greyhood.

All the while, he had been watching the enemy-mink and Dusk. For the sake of his mother he had put up with the stranger. Now he had seen enough of Oak's carryings-on and was running to attack him.

Watching Greyhood galloping towards them, Oak and Dusk beheld a sight never before seen by either of them. With ears and all his hairs erect, muzzle wrinkled, teeth bared – and dark grey eyes wide with the importance of his doing – the cub ran straight at Oak of Strathall.

Less than a yard from his enemy, Greyhood leapt forward but met only empty space and landed on his mouth and nose, hitting the ground a foot short of his target. Oak had avoided Greyhood's lunge simply by moving backwards – beyond the length of the leap. Now Greyhood felt his scruff in the stranger's jaws and, to his alarm, no matter how much he struggled, he could not free himself. Then, with a twist of his great thick neck, Oak released him and Greyhood landed on his back beside his mother. When he started to roll over to get on his feet Dusk pawed him to lie very still. And Greyhood watched as the big dog looked down and smelt him before moving between the trunks of two beech trees to return to the glade. An instant later he had gone.

Dusk and Oak had met before, for each knew the smell of the other. They had met about two months before Greyhood was born under gorse at the top of the Brae-field. Oak had played and ate with her that February afternoon, and purred and slept with her in the den beside McCourt's Stream that evening, but he left her to serve another that night and another after her. This last he had stayed with, to rear their family of six kits, deep inside the remains of an old bridge in Strathall.

For a long time Dusk stood and looked at the empty space between the two beeches. She wanted to keep Oak's smell but would do his bidding and not return to this place beside the quiet glade. After another minute, and while his mother was leading Greyhood downriver back to their stab-cum-den, his father was killing a big buck rabbit in the Pasture behind the sallies.

THE NEST OF IRON

SOON AFTER first light, when the sun shone on the high bank behind the island of the Ardkill Dam, the cock kingfisher left his nest. Voicing a shrill piping 'chee', he cut a bright blue line past the grey-haired man's hide, glinted tawny brown as he swerved over the Pullens and levelled to bright blue again as he sped through the air of the Boat Hole. Seconds later he was perching on pink legs and feet on the lowest branch of a low holly bush at the tail of McCourt's Stream, eyeing the clear shallows for minnows and stone loaches.

He peered with eyes, shiny brown like the body of a black gnat, from a head as big as the rest of him. His head, deeper blue than the alulae of the jay, held an inch-and-a-quarter-long bill the same sooty black as the bud of the ash. The back of his neck showed the same blue, except for a hint of white like his throat, and his wings were as green as the new unfolding leaves of his holly bush. In the light of the morning sun the water reflected the hue of his breast: browner than the ripest chestnut. And the get-together of all these colours made him look bigger than himself, for he could nestle very comfortably in a man's cupped hand.

The kingfisher was still peering at the shallows when two mink trappers walked the right bank of McCourt's. The trappers were going to examine their cage in the Sandpit and rebait the thing with the head of a Faughan salmon. Instantly, the bird sped upstream ahead of them to return to the safety of the Ardkill Dam.

On the dam's island, inside his hide, the man had slept and, for fear of missing anything of the kingfishers, he awakened at half-past three – just before first light. He had been wide awake when the cock bird left the nest. And hidden within canvas walls, he awaited its return. Very soon, he thought, the birds would be using his perches and he crossed his fingers for luck and readied his camera for the umpteenth time.

The coloured blur of the cock kingfisher returned directly to the nest and for several hours more he watched the comings and goings of both the cock and the hen. Neither used his perches. Then on the cock bird's eighth return the man, holding his breath, saw him alighting – momentarily – on the highest side-shoot of the branchlet of sycamore. By the late afternoon both kingfishers were using this perch – sometimes for only a few seconds, sometimes for a few minutes. During the early evening, as if to pose for the excited watcher's camera, the cock used the lowest side-shoot to gaze at the shallows. Soon after, he splashed into the water and returned to the same perch to kill and swallow a stone loach.

About half an hour after sunset, when kingfishers retire and minks get up to all kinds of devilment, Greyhood and Dusk stood and stared at the Ardkill Dam. There they saw the grey-haired man and the great still bird that looked like a heron. And again they observed a strange happening: they saw the man tumbling and attacking the bird until it was gone.

With his tent and other gear gathered, the man left the island and the minks watched him go. He was pleased because his perches were good. After wading the bright shallows and climbing a low bank in the shade of the island's foliage, he turned his head and took his leave of Gosheden's moon.

In bright moonlight Greyhood and Dusk ran through the shallows behind the dam's island and climbed onto the right bank. On the same bank, from forty yards upriver, two fishermen were coming. The minks saw them and hurried away towards the Pullens; there they hid themselves between bracken and bramble. Soon the fishermen waded the throat of the Pullens, climbed the left bank and walked towards the Berryburn Bridge. When the anglers had gone the minks leapt over the narrow stream called Madam's Burn to walk the right bank of the Boat Hole. Greyhood did not know this bank and closely followed his mother as she moved towards Brolly's Burn, and side by side they crossed over to hunt the Sandpit.

Unworked for many years, birds and other animals used the pit all the time. Reed buntings, larks, pipits, tits, finches and moorfowl – as well as frogs, newts, mice, rats, rabbits and visiting stoats and minks – enjoyed the place. Bare patches in the centre of the bed of the place, between ferns and bramble and the like, were caked hard and cracked all over. In other parts the pit was damp and showed rushes and sedges; a scattering of beginning sycamores; young alders and birches; willow and a mixture–maxture of other plant life. Also there, in the damp ditch-side of the Sandpit, baited with the head of a Faughan salmon, tied to the stem of a sturdy alder, stood a mink cage covered with dead bracken.

Put there in the late afternoon of the ninth day of June, the cage had attracted rats galore. Since the week of the June Fair, after the heavy flood-water, fourteen rats and a she-stoat had died attempting to rob the cage. Now, in the early hours of the sixth day of July, the cage would attract its first mink.

Greyhood and Dusk pushed themselves under gorse to peer at the Sandpit's nearest parts, and to listen and smell the air. There they settled into stillness and stayed awhile, for the bright moon lighted the place and a mild north-westerly carried the air into their lie. But the air was empty of food-smells and sounds, and nothing moved except for the taller plants trembling in the soft breeze.

When the minks entered the Sandpit they ran into a nettle patch in the centre of the place. There they looked about them and saw nothing of interest but, searching the air for more, found another strangeness: the air carried the scent of fishes from the damp ditch.

Dusk turned her face towards the ditch and, opening her nostrils to be sure of herself, fixed her stare on a clump of brown bracken. She smelt the fishes of the river and could not know their reason for being in this dry place. Greyhood also stared at the ditch. He knew this smell as food and wanted to eat it but the bitch pawed him to wait. She turned her head to the left to face the river, flared her nose, and then very slowly moved her head from left to right. She dropped on to her belly and lay there, for the thickest smell belonged to the damp ditch. Sensing his mother's concern, but not knowing any reason for it, Greyhood lay down beside her and licked his front paws. But Dusk did not wait long. Very hungry and cautious and most curious, she led Greyhood out of the nettle patch towards the clump of brown bracken, close to an alder on the nearside of the ditch.

As Dusk peered into the bracken she saw, of a sudden, a fish staring out at her. She hurled herself forwards to crush the head of the thing in its nest. Greyhood moved to follow her but a loud noise slapped his face, moved him backwards and made the bracken fall

68

apart. A shock ran through him from muzzle to tip of tail, leaving him breathless on trembling legs. He sat on hunkers and looked at his mother, and waited for her to comfort him. But while he looked and waited, he saw her dropping the fish. Then he watched her struggling in every direction, as if to push the air away. He sensed her alarm and rushed forward to help her, but a rigid cobweb-like thing prevented him from touching any part of her.

The half-eaten head of the salmon lay there still, at rest, and the bitch struggled to reach outside her own length and girth to be with Greyhood running round and round the fish's nest of iron. At short intervals, until just after first light, Greyhood and his mother kept trying to split the web asunder, but it stood firm and made the sound of the Faughan's dipper when they clawed at it.

Then not knowing what to do next, the two minks lay down to rest awhile. Greyhood slept. Beside his mother's cage, with chin on tail, he just closed his eyes and slept. Inside the cage, bruised and exhausted, Dusk blinked at Greyhood and then she turned her head towards the call of a kingfisher speeding downstream from the Ardkill Dam. When the sun lightened the rest of the sky she watched the Sandpit coming alive. Everywhere birds made noises and used the bushes and the air; rabbits hopped from cover into clearings, nibbled at grass, and then hopped back again and out of sight; bees buzzed about brambles and tall foxgloves; hoverflies hung near benweeds and a couple of early orange-tips flitted all over the place. All the while, Dusk found increasing difficulty in keeping her smarting eyes open and her wits about her. Eventually she ate the remains of the salmon's head and fell asleep.

The sun rose, shone across the Sandpit and sent dungflies, greenbottles, bluebottles and houseflies to waken Greyhood and his mother, but the minks slept soundly. Only when the sun moved higher, to touch them itself, did they uncurl themselves awake. Then with eyes and wits dull in the bright light and growing heat, they stood on aching paws. Instinctively Greyhood ran for cover and Dusk tried to follow him.

Forgetful of his mother and her plight, he ran as fast as his aching shoulders and limbs would allow. He wanted to drink Faughan water and return to sleep in the stab-cum-den in the

69

Green Meadow. He was thirsty and sore and tired – most of all he was tired. He took a short cut along rabbit padding and quickly scrambled into a clump of heavy knotweed, out of the sunlight. There in the shade, feeling much relief, he remembered his mother and waited for her company. Before a minute had passed he fell fast asleep.

When Greyhood ran towards the knotweed Dusk had moved to follow him but found her way barred. Instantly alert, a shudder of fear ran through her as she recalled the wasted efforts of the night before when they both had tried to break the cage open. Now in brilliant sunlight she pushed and snapped and threw herself at the walls of the thing. But she could find no way out of the cage. Swimmy with exhaustion, she sank to the floor, lowered her head between front paws, let out a deep sigh and purred in her misery.

DUSK IS GONE

WHEN THE sun was at its height two men walked the right bank of McCourt's Stream towards the Sandpit. One of them was tall, the other was small. The tall man carried a supermarket bag containing the heads of trout and salmon. The small one carried a well-used ferret bag: a green canvas purse with a wooden base showing air-holes. The bag held two drowned minks – two young dogs, one taken from a cage in the Holly Planting, the other from the Beech Wood. The heads of trout and salmon in the supermarket bag would be used to rebait the Sandpit's trap and others. The ferret bag could hold another four minks.

These trappers controlled the mink population along the middle reaches of the Faughan. They trapped to protect small mammals and birds, and for their own enjoyment. And without work and wages, they sold their minks. Any caught mink was drowned and sold to a little fat man for the going price of a grown chicken. He despised minks and wanted them dead for they had killed twenty-three of his chickens, and a bantam rooster, and he had vowed he would kill twenty times twenty-three minks.

Now at two minutes past noon on the sixth day of July the two trappers squeezed themselves through a gap in the knotweed to walk alongside the Sandpit's damp ditch. There they saw the caged mink and moved towards her.

Seeing them coming, Dusk crouched to hide herself in a corner of the cage. Her ears and hairs were erect and her eyes were standing in her head, but the rest of her kept as low as could be. Then the men were overhead and the sight of their great bodies made her leap upright with hairs all standing and tail rigid. She screamed at them and made a bad smell to send them away. She crashed herself against the walls of the cage to show her rage, then she reared herself on hind legs, thrust her face forward with teeth bared and hissed and spat and screamed – daring them to come closer.

'A bitch, an' noisy,' said the tall trapper.

'A looker too. Some smell!' clipped the other man. 'Only a

matter o' time before we get her young. We'll leave them a wadge of her. That'll fetch them!'

Thirty yards away Greyhood slept soundly in a clump of dense knotweed.

The trappers stood and watched Dusk tiring herself.

'She'll not last long in water,' said the tall man. He ran his hand along a length of nylon cord and kneeling beside the alder, he unfastened it.

And Dusk still stood with ears erect and back-hair raised, screaming at the trappers.

The cage was picked up by its iron handle and carried towards McCourt's Stream with Dusk screaming at every step. At the stream the small man tied the length of nylon cord to the stem of a low willow. He let the cage sink in three or four feet of water and, looking down at Dusk, he sneered, 'That'll shut you up.'

And the two trappers, perched on haunches, gazed at the stream and waited for the bitch to die.

In the water of McCourt's Dusk felt cool and safe. She knew this stream and had spent her youth and motherhood loving it. Now, fatigued and sore all over, she turned, head to stream, to face freshness and let her whole body stretch and lift and fall to ease her aches and pains. She moved her legs to dive and turn and roll – to play like always – but to her alarm she could neither dive nor swim. And when she failed to reach upwards to feel air, she knew greater fear than ever before. In her cage below the surface of the stream, becoming more and more distressed, she could not breathe and strange feelings came about her. Hissing noises filled her ears and her head and neck were growing tight; then her eyes bulged and she could see only the hues of darker gloaming. Of a sudden, when the stream became too strong, Dusk gulped and choked and Greyhood was left alone.

PART TWO

GREYHOOD IS ALONE

O N THE bank of McCourt's Stream the trappers watched
Greyhood's mother drowning. They watched the stream
trying to wash her away. They watched her growing feeble
and gulping. They watched her being lifted to choke against the
ceiling of the cage. They watched bubbles and, when the last
bubble had come away from her and burst, they retrieved the
cage.

Dusk was tipped out in a huddle to lie bedgraggled across leaves
of plantain. The small trapper kicked her body straight and the
tall man, squatting beside her, unfolded a penknife. He cut
through the ankle joint of her left hind leg. He did not make a
clean cut — he just hacked it off. Kneeling, he rubbed the paw
against the raw ankle stump until it was bloody and promised,
'This'll fetch her young all right.'

Dusk was thrown into the ferret bag and her severed paw was
used to bait the cage.

Now everything was ready and the trappers returned to the
Sandpit. They placed the set cage in its usual position close to the
damp ditch. Then they covered the cage with the leaves of buckler-
fern and fastened the nylon cord to the stem of the young alder.
Then they moved out of the Sandpit, strolled downriver past
McCourt's and the Brae-field, and took Dusk away with them.

All day Greyhood had slept in the depths of knotweed. When
the sun was sunk behind Slievekirk he stretched himself awake,
and missed his mother. Quickly he got to his feet and peered
through the knotweed. He was very thirsty and hungry and
curious. He galloped to the edge of the Sandpit and crouching, he
searched the gloaming. Soon he felt the smell of Dusk coming
from a hidy-hole in the bracken near the damp ditch. Satisfied that
she was nearby, he ran to the water to quench his thirst and then
slithered from the edge of the ditch to play with his mother. But a
few lengths short of the hidy-hole he stopped and stood on all
fours to stare at the ferns. His mother's air carried the scent of
stale blood and the ferns gave out a fresh smell of rat. And now he
could smell the sour air of humans. He rushed forward and

exposed the cage from its covering of ferns, and there, within iron walls, a doe rat was eating his mother.

While travelling along the damp ditch, the rat had recognised the smell of bloody meat. She sat on hunkers and sniffed the air, and then ran through rush and sedge towards the clump of bracken. When she ran swiftly inside the cage to collect the meat the door snapped shut. Now she turned away from the remains of Dusk's paw to squeal at Greyhood.

Seeing the rat, Greyhood tried to kill her through the walls of the cage. But when he heard the familiar sounds of iron clinking and the rat did not run away he crouched in the fallen bracken. Remembering his mother's failure to escape from this cage, and his failure to enter it, he stared at the she-rat and closed his jaws. It was time to go. He left the Sandpit and crossed Brolly's Burn. Alone, without his mother, Greyhood would need all his wits about him.

Shortly after midnight, in bright moonlight, Greyhood killed a she-rat in the Green Meadow. He ate most of the rat's belly and took the rest of her to the stab-cum-den. He sat by the entrance to the den and waited for his nose to clear. The rich fleshy taste of the rat's underparts had made it stuffy.

For a long time he sat by the den, listening through a quiet breeze to the voices of other things. He heard the Faughan's water streaming away from the Ardkill Dam. He heard the shrill squeaks of pipistrelles just over his head and looked up at them. He heard rabbits and rats and mice and beetles, and other less interesting things. Again he listened to the Faughan. The voice of the river kept on and on. Then, coming from the throat of Leg na gun, he heard the sounds of night fishermen. He knew the voices of rods and reels, and waited to hear fishes splashing after them. He knew the sounds of fishermen under trees and over water, and through water and over gravel and sand. Again he listened to the river hurrying from the dam and cocked both ears to follow its sounds. Now he felt the air drumming, and an instant later, when the screech of a barn owl reached his ears, he sat bolt upright and ran into the den.

There Greyhood bided his time for the night was young. He could not sleep for he was not tired. He just hid and listened. He was not afraid of the white owl but obeyed the ways of his mother. He did not miss Dusk – she was gone now. He was alone but she had taught him well. He could swim and climb and hide, and stalk and kill without any mercy. His kit-hood had ended.

OAK AGAIN

FROM THE last few days of his second month, Greyhood's fur had mostly darkened to a smoggy grey lustre and his shape had changed too. His kit-fat had almost gone and his chest, shoulders, and rump had broadened. He weighed more than a pound and a half and would be slightly heavier than average in adulthood. Already he was bigger than any Faughan she-mink. Now, a few days older than three months, he stood three and a half inches on partly webbed feet, and like all of his kind, each foot held five toes. His body, low and lithe, had lengthened from just longer than two inches at birth to ten times that length from snout to tip of bushy tail, which looked more than half a foot long. His face was lengthening too and noticeable pale grey whiskers were reaching out from a muzzle the sooty colour of the darkest cloud. Teeth like hard clear crystals of quartz filled his strong jaws.

He was a wild American mink: a feral mink, but blue-grey smudges on his lower lip, chin, throat, chest and belly distinguished him from the others of his kind along the Faughan – for they showed white badging. His ears, short and set close together, were the same deep velvet-like charcoal as his back, flanks and tail. His shoulders were distinctly grey. His eyes were deep grey with shiny blue-black pupils; and, except for his charcoal paws, his underparts were the same colour as wood-ash: like the grey back of the hooded crow. He had assumed the shades of his maturity and looked like no other mink along the valley of the River Faughan.

Just before one o'clock in the morning Greyhood swallowed mouthfuls of the she-rat remains. He crept out of the den and sat by a thistle patch to look and listen through a gathering breeze for the white owl. But the thing had gone and bats were using the sky. He went down the meadow to the river's edge and drank his fill. Again he searched the night and, from a dozen yards upstream, he heard rustling noises through grass. He knew a brown rat had made the noises for the grass grew quiet when the rat left the bank. He watched it swimming towards the dam's island, and let the thing be.

The rat dallied awhile on the nearside of the island and then hurried downstream in the direction of the Pullens.

In the deepest part of the middle of the dam a sea trout turned. Then at the tail of the dam another jumped and at the same time a trout splashed near the island. All the while Greyhood stood and watched. Soon the pool was alive with trout moving with the air. The breeze had shifted from east to south-west and clouds were lowering the sky. The night had become warm and the down-stream breeze was soft with the promise of rain. When the trout had quietened to a taking mood the sounds of busy anglers carried from the glade beside the barley field. Despite the gathering breeze, it was a good night for fly-fishers.

Not knowing what to expect next, Greyhood waited but, impatient and restless after only a few seconds, he emptied himself and licked himself all over. He grew bored and began to search the ground, sniffing green moss; licking strands of algae; peering behind overhanging grass and tugging at bare rootlets. When he turned his face to the river to follow a disturbed blackhead worm the scent of another mink drifted past him. He cocked his head, peered into the thickening air and felt the hairs of his neck and back rising. He became very excited, turned round and round, and then sat still by a low alder and waited for the mink to come.

When Greyhood saw the outline of a big dog mink appearing on the far bank he moved into the alder. He positioned himself half crouched between two boulders and stayed very still.

About ten yards upriver of the kingfishers' nest, behind the dam's island, Oak of Strathall stopped and looked about him. He was agitated and angry, for night fishermen were using his favourite stretch of river. Now he stood exposed on a bare bank above the level of the Faughan's flow and would have to climb down a steep slope to get near the island to find cover and food. But always wary of onlookers, he searched the night. Nothing moved about him except the river below, and a warm down-stream breeze carrying the sounds and smells of the fishermen.

Then Oak ran on for about four yards and stopped again. With ears cocked and nostrils flaring, he stared across the dam at Greyhood's alder. Knowing that the screen of alder offered a good hidy-hole, he fixed his gaze. No matter; he could not see Greyhood for he was too well hidden. Soon Oak began to feel his way down from the bank. He was very slow and very careful. A yard down the slope he stopped and sniffed the air again but felt nothing from across the dam for his own smell followed the breeze. So he made his way down the remainder of the slope, ran through the shallows onto the island and, just short of the dam's edge, he stopped and stooped his head to sniff at the sand. He had picked up the scent of wet rat.

Crouching and motionless save for his hurried breathing, Greyhood had watched the big dog. Now he could see him clearly. Two nights before, upriver, he had seen and smelt the same kind of mink and now he had memories of the fearsome dog of the Quiet Glade. But Greyhood could not know he was looking at his father. He crouched lower and stared at Oak, who was examining the edge of the island nearest the dam. Then tiny, separate ripples, like hatching flies, began to show all over the surface of the water. The rain had come. Instantly, Oak ran to drink from the dam. He drank only a little and quickly returned to sniff at the traces of rat and hurried after them, running alongside the Faughan's flow, before the rain had washed them all away.

Greyhood left the alder, swam across the dam, ran onto the island, shook himself and followed Oak downriver in the direction of the Pullens. Fifty yards later, hurrying along a narrow shelf of rocky bank under overhanging willows, he found Oak waiting for him.

Quite suddenly, beneath a heavy willow, father and son stood and stared at each other. Oak had been better prepared for the meeting for, after growing tired of tracking the rat, he had turned his head to face the breeze and felt the air of a hurrying mink. So knowing what to expect, he turned his whole body to meet the breeze and waited. Now, without any warning – bared teeth or anything of the kind – he moved sidewards and then forwards and reached for Greyhood's scruff. Greyhood was confused by Oak's sudden lurch and far too slow to avoid the lunge but, instinctively, he turned his head out of the way and raised his left side, and felt teeth sinking into his shoulder. Anger mounting, he twisted his neck and snapped at Oak's throat but missed. Almost at the same moment he felt his shoulder free but his raised scruff in a holdfast, and then found himself hurtling through the air into the river.

When Greyhood struggled out of the middle pool of the Pullens Oak had gone.

THE SHE-KIT FALL

A FIFTEEN-MINUTE walk away, downriver in the townland of Ardmore, stood the weir of the Bleach-green Dam – sometimes called the Ardmore Dam – where a young mink was taking a brown trout out of a polythene bag. The trout, killed a few hours before by a disappointed novice angler who had failed to catch others, had been tossed into a clump of blackberry briar. The lonely she-kit called Fall, like the darkest seed of the chestnut tree, lived in the Holly Planting. She was very beautiful and, nearly three months old, she was alone. Her mother and father, two brothers and only sister, had been trapped in the Planting and drowned in the Bleach-green Dam.

The dam, a broad flat stretching about four hundred yards from the Deep-end Craig to the weir, reached between a daisy field on its right bank and a high birch wood on its left. The field, a furlong wide, separated the dam from the Holly Planting; the Birch Wood, atop a high left bank, lifted itself more than two hundred feet above the river. Immediately before the weir, a small burn into the dam's left side helped the Faughan from Glenkeen to Ardmore. The weir itself, built during the first year of the nineteenth century, sloping fifteen feet high and a hundred yards long, stretched diagonally across the Faughan to direct some of the river through a sluicegate in its far left corner. Two years before, the weir had mysteriously suffered a fifteen-yard tear in its right side which allowed the Faughan to tumble forwards, causing the dam to run shallow and about thirty yards of weir to become an island. Yet when flood-water allowed, fresh-run salmon and sea trout climbed carry steps to join the dam's own brown trout.

Now, in pouring rain, the young she-mink called Fall lay on her belly and began eating her brownie.

A mile upriver Greyhood sheltered beneath a heavy willow. He sat on a rocky ledge above the middle pool of the Pullens. He sat because his left shoulder hurt and it was less painful to sit than to stand or lie down. He was sore and wet and shivering. The burning pain in his shoulder prevented him from shaking himself dry. Now and again he turned his neck to try to lick the hurt away.

But most of the time he just sat in a kind of daze, trying to use his wits, feeling miserable. He would always remember this night and the dog mink who caused him such distress.

Outside his shelter the breeze caused the trees to make rustling noises and made the air, grey with rain, reek of wet leaves and flowers and other unpleasant things. The air made a continuous murmuring of annoyance. Closer to him the sallies and grasses made their own separate sounds and gave their own strong smells. And below him the dark river broke and broke again through the three Pullens, before tailing into the quiet steady Boat Hole pool. All the while Greyhood sat on and grew more miserable. At length, an hour before first light, when the rain had quietened to a drizzle and his hurt shoulder became numb, he left the Pullens to follow the easiest path he could find. He hobbled along the bank above the Boat Hole in the direction of Brolly's Burn.

Near the burn Greyhood killed a rabbit – all swollen and blind and slow with sickness. Having eaten all he wanted and feeling warmer, he moved on faster than before. After crossing the burn he continued following the right bank, past the Sandpit then alongside McCourt's Stream below the Brae-field, and moved towards the Daisy Field. Soon he came to the Deep-end Craig, half ran beneath the great oaks fringing the Beech Wood and stopped at a deep drain into the beginning of the Bleach-green Dam. The pain had returned in his left shoulder but the drizzle had stopped and birds were beginning to make lively noises. He slithered down into the drain to quench his thirst.

Moving from the weir end of the Daisy Field towards the Beech Wood, the she-kit called Fall felt mink in the air. She caught a glimpse of what looked like a young dog climbing down into the drain before the field. She remembered her brothers and hoped that this mink might be one of them. Fall paused to rub her face across her right forepaw, as if to clear her nostrils and eyes, and then ran behind a clump of tall benweeds. There she stood to get a better view of the dog. Then she saw Greyhood and seemed to forget her brothers, or seemed not to be disappointed, for she became excited when he grew near and hurried from her hidy-hole to leave loneliness behind.

After climbing out of the drain, Greyhood found the scent of another mink. Remembering Oak, his left shoulder tightened and he moved on very slowly, rigid with tension. Of a sudden, with the coming of first light, he saw a young she-mink hurrying towards him and knew a better excitement. Stirred by the sight of her and sensing friendship, he wanted to creep forward to meet her – lest he frightened her away. Instead he began to run. Knowing the ways of her brothers, Fall expected the meeting to be a rough-and-tumble affair. So as Greyhood grew nearer she stopped and seemed to bob and weave in her tracks, and got ready to bounce out of his way.

Within fifteen yards of her, Greyhood misread Fall's strange behaviour and felt both surprise and disappointment for she appeared to be getting ready to do battle.

Not having had brothers or sisters, and having only once seen his otter-cousins at play, Greyhood knew very little about the games of cubs. He knew only the games of grown-ups. He had learned much about lurching and lunging, and scruffing and turning over – but only in battle. Once he had fought an army of rats; twice he had battled with Oak of Strathall; now he must fight again. He had not expected this she-kit to fight for he knew the ways of dogs and bitches. He had seen Oak with Dusk and knew their kinds of exchanges. He expected this waiting bitch to lie down and let him touch her.

When two yards away from her, Greyhood paused to match Fall's every move. And then with a sudden lunge he reached for her scruff and threw her over. A moment later, standing with legs on each side of her, he looked down at her.

Now on her back, breathless, Fall returned his stare. She started to roll over to wriggle herself free but felt his right forepaw arriving heavily on her chest. He wanted her to stay still. She was very confused and a little bit afraid. She felt his pad getting heavier and becoming warm. She was very uncomfortable but stayed where she was and looked up at him. He stood very quiet and still, with lowered head, examining her all over. His nostrils and cheeks were all aflare and his mouth was half opened, but above all his eyes were friendly like the shadows of evening. His look chased her fear away and confusion left her, and she knew what to do. She reached her head forward and licked his paw on her chest, and felt his pad leaving her alone. Her first and second touches had made the paw start trembling but answering her third, the paw set her free. Then she spoiled it all: she bit Greyhood on his sore shoulder and pretended to run away. Ten yards away, she stopped to turn and started bobbing and weaving and bouncing again.

Greyhood just stared at her. He was sore and tired, and she had hurt his shoulder. He had tholed enough already. He would ignore her and her strange games for the light had come and rain was starting.

So Greyhood turned his back on Fall and moved along his own line towards the Deep-end Craig. But she followed and caught up with him before he got that far, and close to the deep drain he felt her touches again. He returned them and went with her to a den where stoats once lived, under the ground beneath two holly trees in the Planting. Soon afterwards, huddled together like young sister and brother, they fell asleep.

SALMON POACHERS

A LL THAT morning and afternoon drizzle and showers and more drizzle helped the rain of the previous night to swell the Faughan's headwaters. About five minutes past five o'clock the sky began to clear and the breeze settled, but agitated streams from hill and moorland, filling feeding-burns and drains, were lifting the Faughan above its own level. At six o'clock a strong wind came and brought more clouds and rain. It rained very hard for three hours and, all the while, the river was rising. Before the rain stopped the Bleach-green Dam rose three feet. And after the downpour, when Greyhood and Fall left their den they found the weir – beginning island and all – under brown water.

It was another powerful flood, angry and roaring and carrying stolen things lifted from the banks and beds of the Faughan's earlier streams and pools. It tore the grey-haired man's branchlet of sycamore perches from below the kingfishers' nest and carried it away. Ten minutes after two o'clock in the morning it stopped rising and left itself six inches too low to touch the kingfishers' nest-hole. It had failed to reach the den beside McCourt's Stream but reached over the right bank of the Bleach-green Dam and brown trout used the nearest thirty yards of the Daisy Field.

It was a good flood: not as high as the flood in June but fresh enough to make hundreds of salmon and thousands of sea trout ready to leave Campsie's brackish water to hurry all the way to Ardmore. The fishes would run when the spate fined down: when useless floating things and bad smells and tastes went away to the Foyle.

Greyhood's shoulder was all right again and Fall and he enjoyed themselves that night. From before sunset until daybreak they stayed in the Daisy Field. Some of the time they prowled and hunted. Most of the time they played. Yet by first light they had filled their bellies with wood mice and brown trout. At daybreak, when fishermen came to spin the dam's fining water with artificial minnows and chrome and copper spoons, Greyhood and Fall went home.

When the spate had fined down, the first fishes climbed the carry steps of the Bleach-green weir. Within the next half-hour two salmon, a score of sea trout and three big brownies lay dead in canvas bags. Apart from the brownies these fishes had come upriver from the nearest stretch of the Faughan's middle reaches – from the pools and streams to Bessie's Dam in the place called Drumahoe. Soon others arrived from as far as seven miles away and several of them were caught. From mid-afternoon through early dusk another eight salmon, thirty sea trout and eight big brownies were killed in the Bleach-green Dam. These salmon and sea trout were the Faughan's newest returning fishes and had carried lice all the way from the sea.

That day for fishermen had been the best yet. The salmon and trout were easily caught – taken from most of the streams and pools along twenty miles of the Faughan's stretch, from tidal water to the bridge called Ballynameen outside the village of Claudy. The first had been caught just before dawn after moving round the very first bend of fresh water into a dark pool called the Black Spool. It was an eight-pound cock salmon, like a bar of silver. Then four sea trout were killed. Beyond the Black Spool, salmon and sea trout were taken from thirty pools with good streams all the way to the Bleach-green Dam. And many others were caught running towards Claudy.

That day for trout and salmon had been the worst yet. Many up-and-coming parents were killed. Even so, many more had escaped and many others were arriving. But the early hours of the next day brought problems too, for as soon as the fishermen went home the poachers came.

By early morning the Faughan had dropped two feet and left the Daisy Field without brown trout. The place kept big puddles but the dam held what was left of the flood; and a few trout and salmon were still climbing white water over the full breadth of the carry steps.

At about twenty minutes past one o'clock, shaded from moon-light, Greyhood and Fall lay side by side in the depths of a willow tree. They lay staring at the Bleach-green weir. They were hiding, for after hunting the Holly Planting they had seen quiet men leaving the Birch Wood to cross the weir, and Greyhood had led Fall into the willow and pawed her to be very still.

Now one of the men was walking past the willow. He wore waders and made squelching sounds as he walked on towards an old iron gate at the downstream end of the field.

Greyhood and Fall lay on and watched and listened.

Five other men stood apart on the sill of the weir, like a wire-and-post fence, ten or twelve yards of white water separating one from the other. They wore waders and held long-handled gaffs. The men, all waiting to cleik passing salmon, looked down the carry steps and stood still and quiet.

Beyond them on a layde wall, next to the sluicegate in the far left corner of the dam, another man stood looking about the place with a potato sack in his hand. The sack would hold six or seven salmon. Two other sacks lay on the wall.

The man who had walked past the willow now stood leaning against the iron gate at the end of the Daisy Field. He peered into a narrow laneway which followed nearly three hundred yards of the Faughan's right bank from the Bleach-green Bridge: sometimes called the Iron Bridge.

The man at the iron gate and his friend on the wall of the layde were lookouts. Only a few hours before, two bailiffs were seen near the Bleach-green Bridge and might still be nearby.

The broad skim of water over the sill and down the weir's slope was empty of trout and salmon. The heavier downpour from the weir's torn right side onto the gathering pool below held no signs of ascending fishes either. But waiting fins, dark and upright, jagged the pool's surface. Hundreds of sea trout and dozens of salmon were waiting awhile to let their sides feel the best way to go. Soon their heads would shake shudders from snout to tail and powerful tail-wrists would provide propulsion.

Greyhood and Fall watched the men on the weir and saw one of them lifting his right arm, pointing at the pool below him. The others turned their heads to stare. A grilse – a maiden salmon without much sense – was trying to climb the apron of heaviest water from the weir's torn side. She had leapt from beneath the downpour, hung five feet up the fall for a second or two and then flopped down into the pool. Again and again she tried and failed. The men on the sill returned their gazing to the weir's easier routes and waited for the more experienced salmon.

Trying to make sense of it all, Greyhood and Fall looked on.

Then the sea trout started running: cutting through white water, half covered. The slope of the weir seemed to crawl with them. The breadth of the weir was agleam with them. They sped upwards, sometimes bouncing and leaping, and shot past the poachers' legs into the deeper water of the dam. Among them were grilse, like big sea trout after a year in the ocean, with graceful bodies and slender wrists. The men on the sill had left the trout and grilse unhindered. It would have been futile to try to catch them: only a fine-mesh net could have prevented their escape. But when the mature salmon ran, led by the strongest and determined to travel on despite bare backs and sides, the poachers went to work.

Thirty-nine salmon died that night on the sill of the Bleach-green weir. Stabbed through silvery sides, open gills, bellies, heads and tails, there were far too many for the three potato sacks to hold.

Later that morning a boy was caught fly-fishing the streams below the weir without a licence and permit. After taking his name and address and confiscating his grandfather's rod, two bailiffs left the boy crying.

By early evening the Faughan had dropped and the water moved slower and warmer. Sea trout and salmon still ran but only as far as the next stream would allow. They could not attempt to climb into dams for the weirs were nearly dry again. During the later gloaming they stopped running altogether and many were showing in narrow lies where they were easily snatched; but returning night fly-fishers scared the poachers away. At midnight Greyhood and Fall heard anglers in the streams beyond the weir, but the weir itself was still and the dam was quiet.

The moon had its dark side towards the Bleach-green Dam and stayed that way for another night, but the Faughan was kept bright with older light from the stars. After the twelfth day of July, the moon reappeared as a slim crescent. That same night knew fewer fly-fishers for the trout had scattered upriver. The last heavy run of trout had passed and the drums of Orangemen heralded the start of serious salmon fishing. It was the time when veteran Faughan anglers always tell: 'When you hear the Twelfth, go after salmon.'

For a few nights more the trout fishers used the dam; but then Greyhood and Fall enjoyed much freedom.

THE BADGER

ONE CLEAR and breezy night, a week after the flood, when the new crescent moon appeared Greyhood and Fall grew tired of the Daisy Field and they went into the Beech Wood. After crossing the deep drain they followed a well-trodden path leading towards a sandy knoll. Along the way they grew more and more curious. The downpours and drizzles had made the dark path slippery and allowed the claw marks of others to show themselves. Dead leaves and woodrushes lining the path carried signs of birds and strange smells. Greyhood and Fall continued following the path to discover more.

Thirty yards later, where the path became narrower, they found coarse strands of grey and black hair on spikes of gorse and smelt body-scratching on the bark of an old beech. The minks sniffed at the hair and the tree and they were puzzled. They sensed air of a familiar kind: almost like their own but nearer to the air from damp rotting leaves. When they found black-green dung in a broad scrape in mulch they flared their nostrils and grew more and more cautious. And when a heap of well-used leaves mixed with dead grasses and ferns gave out the same musky smell, they stopped and sniffed, but then continued along the path. Soon they saw six or seven large burrows in a hump of sandy ground and heard strange grunting noises. Out of the darkest burrow, like twin shafts of moonlight, a great face suddenly appeared. They turned tail and ran, and ran as fast as they could. They had seen a most frightening thing and galloped all the way to their den in the Holly Planting.

It was the same badger-cousin – the big boar, the biggest and oldest along the middle reaches of the Faughan – who had eaten Greyhood's brothers and sisters three and a half months before.

The old badger watched Greyhood and Fall running away towards the Daisy Field and then waddled off in the opposite direction to prowl and hunt the Brae-field.

THE STOATS

BEYOND THE Bleach-green weir the Faughan streamed for about a hundred yards past alder, willow and a lilac tree to reach the red-brick buildings of the Bleach Works. These buildings occupied the left bank for another two hundred yards, and stopped where the river ran under the Iron Bridge to become the pool called Wee Kilcargay.

Here in July, along this stretch from the weir to the bridge, a grey heron sometimes fished. And a pair of Irish dippers, like big wrens who flew like kingfishers between the weir and the bridge, had their mossy domed nest – the size of an adult hedgehog – fixed to the underside of the bridge. Grey wagtails also used this stretch, flighting up and down the streams from stone to stone, dancing all the while. The wagtails had their homes in holes and on ledges along the lower walls of the red-brick buildings.

Running under the bridge, the river moved through Wee Kilcargay and past a lane down the left bank called the Bridle Path, to become Big Kilcargay in the townland of Ballyshasky.

On the right bank of Big Kilcargay in the hollow of a decayed lonely beech, nine fiery-brown Irish stoats lived in a nursery. Eight young, all born at the start of May, were still living with their mother, all of them learning to fight and kill any unwanted thing. Their mother, a very fierce bitch, belonged to the daughter of a family reared in the Holly Planting, but when minks took over their den the bitch left the Planting with her brothers and sisters to join the stoats of Kilcargay.

Sometimes family parties of stoats – from both sides of Kilcargay – joined up to terrorise birds, rats and mice from the Iron Bridge, along the banks of the pools called Lapping Room and Tailrace, to the beginning of Bessie's Dam before Drumahoe. Most times they preferred to hunt alone.

During the seventeenth evening of July, about an hour before sunset as she was returning to the nursery, the bitch stoat saw a buck hare crossing into the lane to the Daisy Field. Quietly she followed, waiting all the while for him to reach open ground. Had the hare seen her behind in the laneway he would have jumped sidewards through hedging and escaped. Now, in the open field and sitting still, he would lie down and die. Without pausing, the stoat moved under the iron gate.

While crossing the Daisy Field from the Holly Planting, Greyhood and Fall had stopped behind a clump of benweeds to look at a strange bouncing animal. They saw something like a rabbit jumping into the field through the lowest rails of the gate. Just into the field the hare stopped, sat on hunkers to look about the place and gave the minks a better view. For them the thing looked like a buck rabbit. He was grey-brown with hardly any tail but his legs were far too long and his ears were too short. His body was bigger and looked stronger than the body of a rabbit, and his head was too broad and too long. Greyhood and Fall kept on looking.

They saw a small red-brown animal, with white throat and chest and belly, creeping under the gate into the field. Immediately, they recognised this other thing as a kind of fitch, a she-fitch, and they watched her moving towards the hare. She was far less than half his weight and size but she was going to attack him. Greyhood and Fall stayed where they were but sat more upright, straining their necks to see more.

The hare turned his head to look at the fitch and then he behaved in the strangest way: instead of standing up to fight or run away, he lowered his ears and body and lay down flat to hide his face. There he stayed, still and stiff with fear, and cried out in terror. After standing beside him awhile, the stoat tore his neck veins and started licking his blood away. Soon she would lick his voice away.

All the while the hare seemed to try his best to please. His squeals had quietened to choke-like whimpers and his heaving body and restless legs had stilled themselves to occasional twitching. Then his voice was torn away with mouthfuls of throat muscles but, before the stoat could swallow the flesh, Greyhood and Fall had left the benweeds. They too were hungry and the screams of the buck hare had made them ravenous. Seeing them coming, the stoat fled from the field, under the gate and into the laneway towards Kilcargay.

Greyhood and Fall hurried towards the still buck, and greyback crows and magpies crossed the river from the Birch Wood. The minks saw them swooping and were wondering what to do when poachers jumped the drain beyond the Deep-end Craig. So Greyhood and Fall never went near the hare, they crept under the iron gate instead and followed the scent of the red fitch. Within seconds the magpies and greybacks fought for the torn buck but one of the poachers took the hare away to feed three polecat ferrets.

When Greyhood and Fall reached Kilcargay's right bank they met many pathways through the hazels. One path, straight into the grove, rough and open and made by fishermen, led down to Wee Kilcargay below the Iron Bridge. The other paths, less noticeable but smelling of fitches, zig-zagged and branched and met all over the place. At first Greyhood and Fall were very cautious and moved slowly into the place, then they relaxed and started to romp. Soon they were thoroughly enjoying themselves: going separate ways, following different paths and meeting each other and rolling in play.

And while Greyhood and Fall were romping together and running after one another, every stoat in Kilcargay heard them and left their nurseries to kill them. Soon nine pairs of angry eyes were staring at the minks from above and behind, and others were appearing all the time to surround them. Two minutes later, when the circle of red fitches had been completed, they all stood still, waiting for their most offended member to signal the attack. The adult bitch from Big Kilcargay screamed a shrill 'yackety-yak', sprang a yard nearer the minks and then stayed still. And all the other stoats did the same to tighten their ring around Greyhood and Fall.

The sudden sounds and smells of danger all around them had startled the minks into stillness and seeing nothing they were scared and puzzled. The sudden single outcry had surprised them and the yakking of many voices from every direction heightened their alarm. They stood still and grew more and more frightened and the gathering scent of threat caused them dread.

Greyhood stood his ground, hairs all raised, moving only his eyes; head and body slightly lowered ready to spring into action. Fall stood still as well but after a few seconds she started her bobbing and weaving and Greyhood turned his head and stared at her in alarm – for the very instant she started her dancing the air whispered itself into a silence. Then, just as the sun set, out of the stillness a big bitch stoat and three young dogs leapt screaming and tumbled Fall onto her back beneath them. Unable to get free, Fall squealed.

At that moment Greyhood sprang forward and caught the bitch at Fall, and bit into the thing's neck, leaving her paralysed from neck to tail. A big dog stoat took her place and, with three young dogs at Fall already, he did what he pleased. Still, Fall squealed. Then a fifth dog stoat, about to rip her throat, loosened his bite to meet Greyhood and died in rage. And all the time without any fear – while fitches tore Fall apart – others snapped at Greyhood from every side. Spread-eagled under four or five of them, Fall's wits were bleeding away. Greyhood kicked and chopped and bit another to death, and ignored countless stabbing hurts to try to pull Fall free but when she stopped squealing he lowered himself beside her to see her face again. He saw only her eyes. Her nose and mouth had been stripped away and her forepaws, all pulp and blood, lay as if protecting her open throat. Greyhood tried to make her see him but he failed. Fall would dance no more.

Now himself under five stoats, some holding mouthfuls of Fall's chestnut hair, Greyhood felt a great force swelling his insides and let it lift him up through them. Then crazed with pain and rage he screamed at them, and grew a great energy, and maimed with every step he took to reach the anglers' path. Still they snapped at his chest and back, and stayed with him until his legs buckled and he fell, unconscious, down the bank into the cold waters of the Wee Kilcargay.

The Faughan hurried through Kilcargay and took Greyhood away, carrying him through the Lapping Room hole into rocky streams where it scattered beginning moonlight into the Tailrace pool. There, before the shallows of the neck of Bessie's Dam, he was left jammed above water in an upward-sloping cleft in half-submerged rock.

That night otters found him and played and sat beside him, and water-rats stayed away.

For six hours Greyhood slept and felt nothing. Then after daylight had come, he opened his eyes and lay very still. With chin resting on a sill of dry rock and his chest and belly in a trickle of Faughan, he lay weak and confused and sore all over. When memories of the previous night had gathered he looked about him and sniffed the breeze that came downriver from Kilcargay. He left the rock in the Tailrace pool to skirt the hazels along the right bank and made his way across a field choking with thistles to reach the lane before Fall's den.

By mid-morning he lay sluggish in the den, full of the scent of Fall, and dozed off and on. Noon had passed before he fell fast asleep but in the late afternoon he was awakened by the sounds of children playing through the Holly Planting. Although fatigued and aching all over, he stayed awake for the rest of the day.

That night he slept awhile and then went away to move upriver again. He took his time and arrived at the Pullens a quarter of an hour before the kingfishers were due out and about. He moved on along the right bank and past the throat of Leg na gun. Just as the sky was beginning to pale over Slievebuck he climbed down the bank and crossed the shallows before the tail of the Quiet Glade. Then he climbed the left bank and made his way downriver to the Green Meadow. At sunrise he crept into the stab-cum-den and felt safe and fell fast asleep.

OAK IS GONE

THE EIGHTEENTH day of August was warm and sunny, the Faughan was beautiful and young kingfishers were about. They had made their first flight a fortnight before and the river bank was alive with colour. At nearly nine o'clock in the evening, when the little fat man and a tall trapper – with a shotgun in hand – strolled the right bank towards the Quiet Glade, the kingfishers flew away. And at half-past nine that evening the tall man with the shotgun, killed Oak of Strathall. At point-blank range he shot Oak in the head and throat, on the right bank of the Quiet Glade, and the little fat man giggled.

Six evenings before, when shooting men roared at the trees of the Green Meadow and pigeons came to the ground without using their wings, Greyhood had moved upriver. He moved as far as the Barley Field and found the place half-harvested. For more than three weeks he had enjoyed himself hunting the stretch from McCourt's Stream to the throat of Leg na gun, but the shooting men had spoiled it all. Yet the Barley Field was good to him for he had killed many mice feeding on the spilled grain and, during five more evenings, he saw many animals and different kinds of birds and much activity.

Each evening he saw a vixen from Lisdillon Hill and a sow badger from Gosheden's Dungeon Glen. Rabbits and rats and long-tailed mice were about all the while, and two buck leverets and their mother used the upper end of the field. Pheasants flew in from the Wood of Strathall and mallard strolled in from the Quiet Glade. Each evening pigeons and sparrows left at the same time to return to their own places and dusk-hunting sparrowhawks followed them. The pigeons flew to their roosts in the high trees and shooting men brought them down. The sparrows roosted close together near finches in the dense hedgerows and the sparrowhawks, who seemed to know about this, caught them unawares. The place was a hive of activity involving other birds and mammals as well and, all the while, the fruits of nearly every tree and bush were there already or beginning to appear. Even a lone female holly, with her back towards Leg na gun and underparts hiding the entrance to a forgotten rabbit-stab, was heavy with olive-green drupes.

For six days, from dawn till just before sunset, Greyhood had used the stab beneath the holly tree and was comfortable there. For six nights he had prowled and searched the Barley Field with good success. But then, during the later gloaming of the eighteenth day of August, when the Ardkill's barn owl arrived to hunt the place, Greyhood left the Barley Field to cross the Quiet Glade.

Across the Faughan, before climbing through the sallies against the right bank, he smelt the air and knew the scent of Oak of Strathall. He stopped and grew tense, and waited a few moments to make ready for battle. Then just into the Pasture he found Oak and hardly knew him, for the great dog was only a dark brown and white body, all in a heap and battered and torn, without eyes or jaws to cause any threat. Greyhood stood and looked at Oak awhile, and then turned away to move upriver towards the March Hole.

When he crept under a wire-and-post fence to jump a dribbling drain he was leaving Crossballycormack to walk Oak's place along the banks and through the Wood of Strathall. Soon he would lay claim to his father's territory and more. Before long he would use both banks of the river from Gosheden Bridge, upstream of the burn called Ness, to Wee Kilcargay.

WHERE BUZZARDS LIVE

T HAT NIGHT the clouds went away and, above a mist close to the Faughan's surface, strange lights like stars crossed the sky. The satellites were always there but now, in darkening August, with few meteors aglow, the grim steady unblinking stars – overtaking all the others – were easily seen. The night was long and the moon was bright enough to hurry Greyhood across the drain to Allison's Brae in the townland of Strathall.

Alongside the March Hole Greyhood turned his head to look across at the bank through Knockbrack. Noisy movements through bracken and gorse had caught his attention. He lay down behind a thistle patch and stared across the river and waited. He watched a sow badger moving out of the undergrowth in the direction of the Horsey Burn. He recognised her as the badger who used the Barley Field in Ardkill. For several nights he had watched her, but from afar. Now he lay still and stared to get a good look.

Heedless of her own sounds and not bothering to look left or right, the badger waddled downriver. She was making for the Barley Field. A heavy stocky fitch, just under twice the length of Greyhood's body, over twice his height and a score times his weight, she looked massive. From afar her coat had looked dark grey but, from ten yards away, she was black-and-white. Her fearsome face had a black band of hair running along each side of her head. With Fall in the Beech Wood long ago, Greyhood had seen a similar kind of face. Now he looked more closely at the great fitch. He looked at her legs: black like her belly and far too short for her body but powerful things on big front feet. She seemed to shuffle all the while. He looked for her tail but failed to see it for it was short and too well hidden by her shaggy coat. He did not notice the kind of her feet: heavy and broad with powerful front claws on five toes. No matter; he had seen enough to realise that her jaws and body were stronger than anything he knew and he waited to see if she was with any other badgers but she waddled on alone.

During the later evening of the twelfth of August, for reasons best known to themselves, shooting men had killed the sow badger's cubs in Gosheden's Dungeon Glen. The cubs, two boars and a sow, all born a few hours before Saint Patrick's Day, had been finding food for themselves about thirty yards away from the sett. Three months earlier, in the middle of May, a few yards from the sett's latrine, her mate had been caught in a fox snare and bludgeoned to death. And the sow found his battered remains at the mouth of the Horsey Burn. Now, in the early hours of the eighteenth day of August, all alone, she crossed the burn to hunt the Ardkill.

When the badger had left the burn and was out of sight Greyhood crossed the bottom of Allison's Brae, where buzzards lived, to search the Glen of the Guns. All that night he prowled the glen and caught three mice and a young rat, and found a hollow sycamore free from damp. Soon after sunrise, with the mice and most of the rat inside him, he was fast asleep inside the trunk and stayed that way till sunset.

For three nights he got to know the glen and then he moved upriver to spend another full night in beginning Strathall. When the sun had paled the sky enough to make him feel seen, he climbed down from the bank onto dry sand and found a lie under a low shelf of rock.

As soon as Greyhood had crept out of sight four leisurely birds, not as dark but bigger than rooks, with broad rounded wings, made mewling calls over all Strathall. They soared nearly two hundred feet above the tallest trees and looked like eagles in the morning sky. Already, with hooked notchless beaks, they had stripped the meat off Oak and many others as well. And still they searched for healthy dead things. After a while, without a cadaver to eat, they would perch on the lookout for a live rabbit or mouse. They might even flap to the ground for a beetle or worm. But now they sailed above the river for any scared thing to know. From four hundred feet their brown backs and pale breasts were impossible to tell, but their small heads, fanned tails, and finger-tipped wings were enough to see. They moved in a circle like leaves in an eddy knowing only freeness for they moved without wing-beats.

More than three months before, on the ninth day of May, two

buzzards had built their nest in the fork of a larch on Allison's Brae. The nest, bulky and almost three feet wide, made of bare branchlets and bracken and lined with woodrush, stood seventy feet above the ground. On the twelfth day of May they decorated the nest with fresh branchlets covered in leaves. In the later afternoons of the sixteenth and eighteenth days of May two eggs were laid, dull white with reddish-brown markings – the size of the eggs of farmyard chickens. From then on both parents sat, with the hen sitting most, until the early mornings of the twentieth and twenty-second of June when the buff-grey chicks appeared. For the first few days the hen stayed with the chicks and gave them food from their father. But when the chicks needed more both parents brought food. And at least once a week they brought fresh greenery to add to the nest. During the eighth day of August, the exact time is not known, the full-fledged young followed their parents into the Faughan sky. And now a fortnight later they could sail and soar and veer and roll, like their grandparents used to do when they were the first buzzards to be seen along the valley of the Faughan.

WITH IN-LAWS

O N THE night of the twenty-third day of August, in the light of the full Grain Moon, Greyhood continued upriver. Now and again he dallied awhile to sniff at scats but when the smells of minks filled the air, a feeling of excitement grew all through him. And leaving a nettle-bed, when he saw four minks, his excitement grew greater. Up ahead, an adult bitch and three cubs were climbing up the bank near the stone remains of an old bridge. Greyhood stopped in his tracks and then moved sideways into a hazel, and saw the minks turning their necks to glance back at the river. When all four had reached the top of the bank he saw them turning their bodies to stand staring at the river. Then Greyhood, too, saw the otters moving into the Bridge Hole pool.

The otters had come downriver from the pool called Jeannie Lyons. They knew the likely holding places for trout and salmon, behind rocks and stumps of trees, and searched them one after another every night. Now they saw minks standing atop the right bank but ignored them. When they had skinned and eaten all the trout they could catch and began moving on downriver they heard the minks returning to fish the shallows again. Still they paid the minks little heed for the pools and streams, with the best runs and lies, had always belonged to them. They would go as far as the March Hole and search the very best places along the way.

In the bright moonlight Greyhood had watched all the carryings-on but neither otter nor mink had sensed his presence and, when the minks had climbed down the bank, he left the hazel to join them. Below him in the shallows of the Bridge Hole, he saw the bitch and her three cubs, and watched them turning their heads up the bank. He stayed where he was and returned their stare.

They were the family of Oak of Strathall, begun after Oak left Dusk to mate in his own townland – his partner, son and two daughters. His mate, his second bitch after Dusk, had come from Tamneymore to live in the den the September before and the kits arrived on the last day of April. Since then, while Oak had lived twenty yards upstream in a disused nursery for stoats, the bitch and her young had continued to use the den in the bridge. There had been two other sons but both were dead – killed together a month earlier in the townland called Legaghory: mauled to death by two Kerry blue terriers who were out for the night. And then, just over three weeks later, the minks of Strathall had lost Oak as well. Now they stared at another dog mink and Greyhood stared back.

The bitch had a flat blue-black coat with a reddish tint to her tail. She would soon lose her tint to become blue-black and glossy all over. Before the Fruit Moon's turn, she would start changing her summer wear for a coat far richer and thicker. No matter; already she looked the colour of the blackthorn fruit and her name was Sloe.

Greyhood climbed down from the bank and Sloe moved away from the cubs to meet him, and she seemed glad for she licked his face and accepted his returns.

The cubs stared at their mother and watched Greyhood's friendly touches but, not knowing what to do, they became fidgety. So Greyhood moved forward to meet the cubs – black-brown like the pods of furze – and felt the touches of the dog called Gorse and his sisters Broom and Whin. Soon the cubs and their mother were fishing as before, taking loaches at the edge of the pool, and licking Greyhood once in a while to keep him from going away.

Three hours after midnight the minks of Strathall crossed the Bridge Hole pool and climbed a steep bank to Legaghory, and Greyhood followed them. There they showed him their trails and the best places to go. They took him to a great humpy meadow where a bleach-works used to stand and led him across its rise and fall to reach an old tailrace trench to the stream into Jeannie Lyons's pool. Along the trench they killed and shared a hedgehog and then found fresh otter spraint. They led him towards Goshe-den Bridge, a quarter of a mile upstream, through rushy beds near great oaks and alongside the Faughan's flow between Humpy Meadow and the banks of Strathall. Midway between the tailrace trench and Gosheden Bridge, across from where the Ness Burn ran, they stopped awhile to watch a big dog otter skinning a two-pound sea trout at the burn's mouth. Almost at the bridge, they examined the chalky scat of a fox and found the lower jaw of a mouse hidden in the dirt. On their return to the downstream end of the meadow, they all ran through a wooded glen where six horse chestnuts had grown for nearly two hundred years. The trees were heavy with fruit. Then they drank from a tiny burn between Legaghory and Gosheden.

At the end of the night they left the Chestnut Glen and Greyhood followed the minks of Strathall across the Bridge Hole pool. At the entrance to their den he went his own way. He went on alone, but not far. He hurried twenty yards upstream to the disused nursery for stoats and fell fast asleep in Oak's bed.

From Allison's Brae to the townland of Tamneymore, stood the dense broad-leaved Wood of Strathall. Planted over three centuries before, it was still inhabited by thousands of living things. There were oak, beech and birch and plenty of ash, elm, sycamore and rowan. Hazel and holly were the most common shrubs, with alder and willow near the Faughan's edge. Laurel-type plants were about as well with pine, larch and spruce. But the most sightly of them all, in a clearing in the centre of the wood, was a redwood called the Fairy Tree. This last, the biggest living thing in the wood, two hundred and seventy feet tall with a massive burled trunk, kept all the other plants away. No matter; the Wood of Strathall was a generous place – everywhere and all the time.

A few minutes before dusk the five minks began hunting the wood and fed very well. And for almost a month they fished the Bridge Hole pool and searched every trail and hidy-hole in the wood and Chestnut Glen – and Humpy Meadow as well. They caught trout and stone loaches at the river's edge; caught a hen salmon with white spots on her face at the tail of the pool; shared ten hedgehogs and pygmy shrews galore and wood mice trapped while stocking their stores. They killed rabbits, destroyed a colony of rats beneath an old stone building at the upstream end of Humpy Meadow and defeated a pack of stoats from Tamneymore.

During that month, when the sounds of summer nights had faded and the air became increasingly chilly, the minks started growing new coats. Greyhood continued to use Oak's den and the others let him take the lead. Sloe ran with him as much as she could and chased Whin and Broom out of the way. Broom was tinier than the others and Greyhood touched her most of all. And he seemed to like his brother Gorse for he showed him how to fight.

In the early gloaming of the twenty-second evening of September Greyhood left Oak's den and the minks of Strathall to go his own way. He moved upriver alongside the wood, drank from the throat of Jeannie Lyons and caught two brown trout. In Tamney-more he crossed the mouth of the Ness Burn before Gosheden Bridge and then swam the Faughan to reach Legaghory.

Sloe and the others searched for him awhile but they knew he had gone and could not feel bothered for they would do the same within the next few days.

THE SILVER EELS

O<small>N THE</small> twenty-third day of September, at forty-two minutes past three o'clock in the afternoon, the sun crossed the celestial equator and day and night became the same length. It was the first day of autumn and the rain started to drizzle. And female eels from the Faughan's headwaters and side-streams and nearby ponds and drains began to move downriver to reach the Foyle.

That morning Greyhood had returned to the rat-pit at the upstream end of Humpy Meadow and slept until the late afternoon. During the early gloaming, he stood across from the Ness Burn and watched great black and silvery worm-like things rolling and wriggling out of the burn's mouth. For fifteen minutes he stood and watched them, and grew more inquisitive all the time. When curiosity got the better of him as he crossed the Faughan to take a closer look he felt things touching his legs and jumped twice the length of himself out of the water onto a dry gravelly bed. He need not have bothered for the eels were not bothering with him. They wanted only to get to the river's mouth and then three thousand miles away to lay their eggs and die.

They had been the elvers of a dozen years before who came to the Faughan to grow big and ripe. Born in the depths of the Atlantic's Sargasso Sea, it had taken them three years to reach the Faughan's mouth. As eggs, and then larvae, they had floated towards Ireland in the surface currents of the North Atlantic Drift. A while later, exactly when is not known, they became glass eels, like transparent worms and just over two inches long. When they turned a yellowish-grey, with long dorsal and tiny pectoral fins, they moved inshore and were called elvers. During March and April, through May, measuring three inches long, they came to fresh water and found their way up the Faughan to become mature silver eels. And then they would return to the west Atlantic on their own spawning migration.

Now in his first autumn-gloaming, standing on a low gravelly bank in a steady drizzle of rain, Greyhood watched the silver eels journeying past him. He saw them as far as the throat of Jeannie

Lyons and the otters saw them too.

All that night the otters feasted – allowing the eels to pass before taking them from behind – leaving only pointed heads on pectoral fins to stare at Greyhood and other interested things. He ate several heads and then killed an eel himself. It was great sport and easily done, and the meat was sweet and very filling.

That same night Greyhood saw his young brother hurrying upriver along the right bank – running away from home. Gorse stopped and looked at Greyhood awhile but then moved on faster than before towards the Ness Burn.

That was the last time Gorse was seen along the Faughan's banks for three weeks later at the head of the Ness, near a wooden footbridge before the place called Loughermore, he was trapped in an iron-wire cage and drowned in the Wee Burn.

In the week that ended September, when mist and drizzle kept the brightest day like early gloaming, Greyhood fed on eels without much effort and hardly slept. By day he used the rat-pit in Humpy Meadow but always got to the river before the otters arrived. By night he fished the Ness Burn's mouth, the outlet stream from Jeannie Lyons and the tail of the pool called the Dog Hole. He killed eels galore – mostly for the sake of killing them.

After the skies of summer, the later-September evenings and nights were noticeably bare. Apart from the Fruit Moon's wane there was little to be seen. No matter; when drizzle and low cloud cleared away for a while winter stars could already be seen creeping above midnight's eastern horizon. Before too long meteors would brighten the Faughan's skies; but the pipistrelles would go away.

On the first afternoon of October, just about four o'clock, when Greyhood found anglers fishing his favourite runs and a grey heron standing in the shallows beside the Dog Hole pool, he moved on downriver as far as the Bridge Hole. Across the pool he found Sloe's den and all the hidy-holes near the old bridge deserted.

Later that afternoon the drizzle went away for a while but came back as heavy rain. Three massive black clouds before a strong south-westerly, and stretching all the way from beyond Sawel Mountain to the mouth of the Foyle, made the day as dark as night long before nightfall. The clouds burst and drenched the valley from head to tail. The rain fell through the evening and night, and fell hard against trees and other upright things but made little impact when it reached the ground, for the drizzled soil would take no more and sent it hurrying to the river. All night the uplands, moors and nearby fields sent their rain with debris to the river and, all the while, Greyhood slept warm and dry in Oak's den.

Just before dawn, while the lightened clouds were moving away over the Foyle's estuary towards the sea, the Bridge Hole pool rose twelve inches. And soon after dawn, when the sky had cleared and the pool was another foot higher, the silver eels were being carried safely to the Faughan's mouth.

The rain stopped but, by eleven o'clock in the morning, the Faughan had risen three feet and was still rising. It crashed and roared over rocky and shallow streams, moving easy, yet grumbling, through the deep pools. It rushed on opaque brown, frothy, littered with branchlets and twigs and loaded with leaves from the ash, sycamore and oak. It carried branches, the stump of an oak, several sheep and other things as well. It was a good flood: good enough to let the silver eels, and salmon and trout, move their opposite ways to spawn.

At two minutes after noon, four feet above its usual level, the Faughan stopped rising. During the second half of the afternoon, when the spate began fining down, the salmon and remaining sea trout began running and fishermen, with spoons and worms and larger-than-usual flies, took fishes all dressed to spawn and full of eggs or milt.

THORN

THAT NIGHT, facing a mild downstream breeze, Greyhood returned to the moonlit Wood of Strathall and killed pygmy shrews and long-tailed field mice. Having gorged himself on silver eels for more than a week, the shrews and mice were tasty. He was enjoying himself and felt good. He moved on into the wood to catch a rabbit or rat for the den and then, near the redwood called the Fairy Tree, found himself becoming tense. He felt a stranger-mink in the coming air and knew the smell of an older dog. Immediately he backed into the depths of a holly bush and, moments later, saw a dog mink crossing the clearing on the nearside of the Fairy Tree. He stayed still and watched the mink stopping to stare at buckler-ferns. Behind a broad-leaved willow the stranger stood motionless and waited. Just twenty yards from Greyhood, he looked fierce and strong, like Oak of Strathall.

The big dog mink was called Thorn: the brother of Sloe and leader of the minks of Tamneymore. Blue-black and sleek like Sloe but twice her height and weight and twenty-six inches from scarred muzzle to tip of bushy tail, he was powerful and threatening. He was a vicious fighter and troublesome neighbour but had learned to stay out of Strathall. Several times he had battled with Oak, who had been a year his senior, and he had lost every time. Now something made him know that Oak was gone; that the woodland was safer than before and that Sloe and her young would let him come and go. Still he stood and stared at the bucklers and Greyhood watched him.

Over a minute passed and the minks and the ferns remained still. Then of a sudden, when the bracken moved, Greyhood watched Thorn leaving the willow to stoop, still and low with legs bent, ready to spring. He had crouched to wait for the hiding thing to bolt or attack. But the thing did not budge – it just kept moving the ferns. Then, with teeth bared and body pressed against rump, Thorn leapt into the hidy-hole and snapped his jaws on the neck of a dog stoat in a rabbit snare. For a split second the he-stoat fought and then died. And an instant later, jumping backwards and forwards and laying the bracken flat, Thorn was struggling to free his right leg from another snare. After a minute of useless attempts to free himself from a noose of insulated flex-wire, he tore open the face of the stoat, and then lay on his belly to gnaw the snare's plastic sheath.

Greyhood had stood and watched Thorn's various struggles. Now he looked at the trapped mink, felt himself trembling all over and abandoned the safety of the holly bush to approach the great dog. As he drew nearer he saw Thorn lifting his head and then his body to fight. Then he stood facing the stranger-mink.

Greyhood saw Thorn coming but, after leaping as far as he could, the dog fell short. Thorn crouched just under a yard away, staring at him and showing bared teeth. Greyhood did not move but gauged the mink's every threat; he watched him very carefully. Again, with jaws wide open and legs reaching forward, Thorn leapt at him and fell short. He fell to the right in a lopsided way but recovered his stance in time to prevent any attack. Greyhood stayed still and wondered at Thorn's strange behaviour. No matter; he would do what he taught Gorse to do – fake and then attack. Soon he knew to keep shifting to the right for time after time Thorn kept falling the other way and the falls were slowing him down. Greyhood moved a yard nearer and let Thorn come, but faked to the left and moved to the right. Thorn was confused, badly shaken and smelling with anger. Greyhood stood within easy reach and waited for him to come again but, growing wiser all the while, Thorn refused to move. For more than ten seconds he refused to move. Suddenly Greyhood lunged forward and made him come, swerved to the right as the dog passed, twisted left again – then round – and ripped Thorn's left ear from back to front. Immediately, Greyhood stood upright and still. All his tremblings had gone. He stood with bloodied teeth and expected Thorn to fight like Oak of Strathall. And, even as Greyhood thought, Thorn leapt at him, ignoring his fake, moved with him to the right and held his left front leg above the shin. Greyhood chopped ten times in three seconds. He chopped at the dog's fierce face and kept chopping until the great jaws fell away. Instantly, he started again and ripped fur and flesh off the crown of the dog's head. Thorn screamed and rolled away but Greyhood went after him and bit into his neck. When he felt Thorn's left legs and head trying to push him away, Greyhood gouged a hole for his muzzle in Thorn's neck and tore every vessel and any other thing he could find. Within moments all Thorn's fierceness was bleeding away and his screams gurgled to a kind of purring sigh. Then Thorn twitched and died near the he-stoat in the bracken.

Greyhood looked about him and washed himself in the spate's fresh water, and let the Faughan carry him to the Bridge Hole pool. He spent the remaining night in Oak's den trying to lick his torn leg better and, at first light, he closed his eyes and fell into a deep sleep – sore and tired.

Brown rats went through the bodies of Thorn and the dog stoat during the night, and buzzards and magpies and greyback crows had the rest of the flesh before noon. But beetles and flies of various kinds found other food to take, for they left the skulls empty and the bones nearly bare before nightfall.

All through the day the Faughan dropped towards its normal level and flowed more quietly than before, changing its colour from peaty black through purple, then golden claret, to become a beautiful amber. And, all the while, salmon and sea trout ran and the fishermen tried to catch them.

Greyhood awoke in the mid-gloaming, feeling a throbbing pain in his left front leg. The wound, an inch-long jagged tear, was raw and red from thigh to shin and tiny black flies and a busy blue-bottle crawled all over it. All day he had slept and dozed on his right side with front legs crossed before him with his chin on his right elbow. He had protected the damaged leg and it let him rest all day, but after easing and then lying numb for a while the thing had come alive and painful again. He turned his face to make it better and licked the flies away. His touch caused much pain but he kept on licking. Soon it eased and he stood upright and then limped into the Bridge Hole and let himself drift like an otter. He watched great fishes, longer than himself, some red, others blue-black, running and leaping through the pool from tail to throat and beyond.

When he had bathed long enough to move without any pain he returned to the shallows to hunt small fish. He hunted in vain and grew very hungry. At length he climbed the bank near Sloe's den and hobbled away to the Wood of Strathall. There he killed a long-tailed field mouse and then rested awhile beneath a laurel bush. His leg had become more painful and his left foot was beginning to swell.

An hour later he was hungry again and left the laurel to hunt leaf litter, but growing very sore and warm, he left the wood to return to Oak's den. Close to home, feeling too hot and becoming dizzy, he lay down and grew frightened. He lay on the anglers' path and knew the dangers of this place. He was more thirsty than before, his chest was moving too fast and his heart was pounding. Then the front of his head throbbed like his leg and his body began to shiver. With much effort he crawled along the path and tumbled into Oak's den to sleep off his fever.

Greyhood slept warm and cold until the following evening and awoke feeling less frightened than before. He felt feeble and more thirsty than hungry, but the throbbing in his head had gone, his chest had quietened and the pain in his leg had become a dull aching thing. In the later gloaming he limped down to the Faughan's edge and drank for a full half-minute from the Bridge Hole pool and then returned to the den to rest again.

An hour before dawn, after drinking from the Bridge Hole once more, he followed his own line to the Wood of Strathall and killed two long-tailed mice and an old rat. An hour after dawn he dragged the rat to the den. He was exhausted and slept until sunset.

When he hunted the Wood of Strathall that night he killed two shrews, a long-tailed mouse and another old rat. Now he was strong and fast and alert. His leg was itchy, the swelling had gone and his hunger had returned. The terrible thirst had left and he was well again.

111

SPAWNING FISH

EVERY DAY for the next fortnight fishermen tried the Faughan's pools and streams and caught many salmon and a few trout, sometimes with black-headed worms and pink worms called brandlings, most times using flies called bugs – shrimp-like things with floss-silk for bodies and badger-hackles for legs. At the close of the twentieth day of October, when the fishing season came to an end, the last of the Faughan's anglers put up their rods for another year and left the salmon and trout to find their own parents' spawning beds.

For ten thousand Octobers, ever since autumn leaves began floating down the Faughan, salmon and sea trout moved upriver to shed ova and milt, to spawn in November through December. There were always stragglers who ran in November; but a tradition observed from the time the Faughan began, brought most of the salmon and trout to their spawning fords by the close of any October. Their excitements grew, and more hormones in each and every fish brought other changes of a physical kind. The trout – both male and female – and the hen salmon grew blackish above and dusky on the belly but, apart from this, they usually retained their normal good looks. It was the cock salmon, or soldier fish, who knew the greatest change of all: the beautiful silvery green of his flanks and upper parts became a dirty copper-and-red colour; the black spots on his flanks and back grew larger; his white belly became a greyish-yellow; his skin grew hard and tough and looked spongy, and many of his scales became buried in it; his snout lengthened and the upturned kype on his lower jaw grew much longer. He always changed in a very marked way to become an ugly fellow.

Mid-October's gales regularly heralded the run-up to spawning. It was a time for courtship, beginning nest-making, chasing rivals and much ritual, and each and every adult fish wore their special dress for the occasion.

During the last evening of October Greyhood watched a female squirrel on the ground near hazels on the river side of the Fairy Tree. She was a red squirrel who had just left the hollow beech near

Greyhood's favourite holly bush. She was busy eating fungi and searching for nuts and berries. A week before, waiting in the holly bush for a doe rabbit to pass, he had watched the same squirrel searching the ground, climbing up and down nearby trees, and he marvelled at her speed. He could easily tell her from the others he knew, all of them red-brown and bushy, for she had only one ear. No matter; she could run faster than any mink and climb trees faster than all the others. Greyhood watched her for another while, and then moved on to examine rabbit dirt and padding through bracken and bramble.

Late that night a strong south-westerly shook Strathall and carried the buzzards' nest from Allison's Brae into the Pasture in Crossballycormack. Soon most of the birds' nests would go, and even the leaves of beech would fall. It was a wild night and heavy rain promised to lift the Faughan again.

In the gathering storm Greyhood left Strathall and crossed the tail of the Quiet Glade, away from Crossballycormack, towards the throat of Leg na gun. Soon after first light he crept into the stab-cum-den in the Green Meadow.

All day alternating showers and drizzle drifted along the valley from Sawel Mountain helping the heavy rain of early morning to lift the Faughan again. By noon the river had risen twelve inches. By mid-afternoon it was another foot higher and, by first gloaming, it had flooded the empty otter holt in the left bank of Leg na gun. An hour before midnight the rain left the Ardkill Dam to drift beyond the Kilcargay pools towards the Foyle but the dam kept rising. It continued to rise until early morning when its island lay beneath brown water and had left itself fifteen inches below the kingfishers' old nest-hole.

It was another good flood, littered with debris and different kinds of dead things, and carrying the first of November's tawny leaves torn from the tallest beeches.

When the rain had eased to a warm drizzle Greyhood crept away from the stab-cum-den to search the Green Meadow. He had run over mud and through puddles to hunt the meadow's riverside but without any success. Then he crept through soaking grass towards the upper end. It was forty minutes before midnight and the rain had recently stopped. Ground-hunters were beginning to search leaf litter for haws and sloes, woodlice and spiders and worms washed out of their homes, and different kinds of slugs and snails out for the night. The place was crawling with food.

The night was warm for November and the upper end of the meadow was lively and crowded but Greyhood, with nostrils reaching for any smells of fur or feather, felt only damp grass and rotting plants. He had stopped midway between the stab-cum-den and a spread of gorse, with a mild downstream breeze across his face, and knew nothing about the things up the meadow before him. He crouched behind a clump of withered benweed and strained his eyes but saw nothing. He moved on and, fifteen yards later, he knew almost everything. Again he stopped and crouched and regarded all before him: lazy rabbits eating snails and lobworms; shrews feeding on spiders, woodlice, worms and insects; long-tailed mice also nibbling at snails and a hedgehog after haws and sloes.

All night long Greyhood killed mice and shrews and, half an hour before daylight, he dragged a doe rabbit to the den.

On the third night of Greyhood's return to the meadow, when the river had returned to its normal level, he saw strange lights striking the belly of the Ardkill Dam and went to discover the kind of them. Finding no explanation in the sky, he crawled to the river's edge and saw the lights coming from the hands of men. Then he saw the leaping fishes caught in a great net and later he watched the men taking the fishes away.

His fourth night in the Green Meadow was pleasant and very dark for the moon was new and the sky was cloudy. Apart from a few shooting stars, tired and nearly spent, the place was perfect for night hunters. Again he searched the upper end of the meadow and killed mice and shrews, and a doe rabbit for the den. He went to bed two hours before daybreak and slept until three hours after noon.

That afternoon he watched a little fat man and two other men looking at the Ardkill Dam and talking like greyback crows. He lay on his belly and watched them peering into the water, shaking their heads, and then climbing the bank to walk in the direction of the Quiet Glade.

That night the barn owl came, white and silent and quartering low, with a slow flapping flight, before gliding along the upper meadow. With a flurry, the rabbits and all the others disappeared, and Greyhood crept into a low gorse bush to crouch and peer. He had seen the thing before for this was the she-owl who had terrified Dusk. Now he watched the owl moving low and slow, backwards and forwards, over the meadow and alighting close by on a post between two bare hawthorns. She perched bolt upright, all orange-buff and white, with large dark eyes watching and flat face listening. Greyhood looked at her and she seemed smaller than before. She did not stay long and after snapping her bill and making a snore, she flapped away downriver crying long and eerie all the way.

She was the owl of the Berryburn Mill who had lost her mate and four young, and was lonely. Nearly three months before, during the twentieth evening of August, shooting men had killed her mate – to be stuffed – and scared her children away. She had laid her first white egg on the second day of May and her fourth, six days later, and she had stayed with them till the eleventh day of June, when all four had hatched downy and white. And her mate had been very good for he fed her all the while. For another ten weeks her mate and young had stayed with her. Then, three days later, the shooting men came and her mate and children went away. Still she used the ledge in the mill, and would stay there for another while.

When another fortnight had passed and more meteors had fallen the Green Meadow lay bright under November's full moon. A gale from the east came across Slievebuck and blew the meadow's beeches bare. It started to blow at dusk and sent the pipistrelles away, and warned them to stay away until March would whistle them back. And Greyhood and his cousins and others went early to bed – some to stay for a month or two.

Many strong winds came during the remaining November nights and left the place black and bare. But the Green Meadow in this dark month, when night borrowed an hour and thirty-nine minutes from day, was good to Greyhood. Now the night air was becoming very cold and his wakefulness was going. Three weeks on, when day and night would start growing apart again, he would sleep contentedly.

115

In the early afternoon of the third day of December a blue-black hen salmon cut a redd in gravel in the throat of Leg na gun. In water barely covering her back she was using her tail and belly-fins to make a wide round hole: twice the depth of any mink and the same width as a mink is long. She had three other redds already, all lying diagonally across the bed of the river, and she kept inspecting them. Then she turned, swam ten yards down-stream, and lay very still – head to stream – in four feet of water behind a half-submerged boulder. Minutes later another hen fish did the same thing and red cock fishes began dunting each other.

In the three days and nights that followed, when the moon offered only earthshine, and a north-easterly wind brought bitter cold and fog, Greyhood stayed indoors. In his happing of new winter coat, and rabbits ready to be eaten, he kept warm and slept and dozed between meals. During the early afternoon of the fourth day, the seventh of December, a restlessness came over him and he crept out of the den and found strange thrushes all about the place. He watched them awhile and then ran to the upper end of the meadow to hunt rabbits. There he saw another strange bird, all chestnut-brown showing green and red, and he made the pheasant fly away. He returned to the den dragging behind him a doe rabbit, then, after looking at fieldfares and other strange thrushes for a while, he went indoors for the remaining day and night.

The cold air from the north and east had brought hundreds of redwings and fieldfares to the valley of the Faughan. There they would enjoy shelter and haws, and other drupes and berries until the end of February and maybe through March.

During the late afternoon of the eighth day of December, Greyhood watched a female mallard arriving at the tail of the Ardkill Dam. He was standing on the high left bank of Leg na gun watching the flashes of salmon, and was about to climb down from the bank when the duck flighted downriver. A grey heron had chased her from the Quiet Glade. Greyhood turned his head and watched the duck landing downriver close to the left bank, near the Pedlars' Well, and he moved towards her. The air was full of her and he felt his mouth filling with lukewarm water. From a clump of brown buckler-ferns, he lay on his belly and peered at her. She looked dowdy – all brown with a patch of blue on each

116

wing, and a dirty-green bill. She seemed agitated and he watched her moving upstream and downstream, then upstream and downstream again, and all the while she kept getting closer to the bank.

Below Greyhood, between the lower bank and a great boulder, was a sandy ledge. It would hide him and bring the duck much closer. He waited for her to move downstream again, then dropped onto the ledge. Again he waited and watched. As she turned to move in his direction Greyhood stayed very low and still. She would not smell him for she did not have that sense – but she might see him. He watched her coming. He would take her paddling towards him for she could not escape backwards. He watched her getting closer and closer and then he leapt. She squawked twice but died before she could flap a wing.

When the mallard was quiet and her head came down with a flop he used the dam's easy flow to help him carry her to the beginning of the old layde to the mill. About a yard before the Faughan left the dam to break into a run, he pushed the mallard into the layde – a dry and sheltered place. There he ate her belly and breast but when the grey heron came over Leg na gun, he started dragging his duck to the stab-cum-den.

Shortly after noon spawning salmon had started laying and fertilising their pinkish and pea-sized eggs in the gravel-bedded throat of Leg na gun. The salmon had taken up residence in the pool's lies before the business of spawning was to be done. Then at noon the hens moved to the first of their redds and the cocks soon followed them.

For three days the salmon were active. The hens then returned to the belly of the pool to rest and grow strong again, but the cocks stayed with their redds – moving from one to another.

BROOM

GREYHOOD AWOKE during the later morning of the twelfth day of December, hearing the kind of sounds a he-fox makes. He felt a woody smell and saw the feet of a great black animal outside the entrance to the den. It was not a fox. Greyhood watched and listened and waited. Then a huge face looked in at him, opened wide, and filled the den with dreadful barking noises. The barks moved the scattering of mallard feathers and made Greyhood crawl tight against the back wall. His ears buzzed and his body trembled. He was very frightened. Still as he could be, with no other exit, he watched and waited. A long black paw came into the den, scraped the floor and walls and searched the air. Then it crept out again. Still Greyhood waited until the voice of a man grew nearer and took the thing away. And at the entrance to the den he lay shivering and watched a grey-haired man with a black dog crossing the Green Meadow. He had not fully recovered from his fright when shooting men, with twelve-bore guns, tried to kill a cock pheasant in the upper end of the meadow. Completely unnerved, he left the stab-cum-den and ran away in the direction of the Berryburn.

He ran past the Pedlars' Well to the mouth of the layde before the dam's ruined weir and followed the trench to the old floodgate. A furlong beyond the gate he saw the gable of the mill and watched rats hurrying round the corner of the wall to get out of his way. He followed them to their hole under the front entrance to the building and stopped there awhile taking in the warm smell of recent rat. He was very hungry but memories from long ago kept him still. He knew this place, remembering the battle with an army of rats, and he ran on along the mill's tailrace and crossed the Berryburn.

Past Brolly's Burn, he found the river low and quiet and he continued close to the left side, beneath the high bank, before swimming sixty yards of slow deep pool. Soon the river became noisy again and he had to tumble a hundred yards of racing water to arrive at McCourt's. He climbed the left bank and sniffed at a large red slug in a mink's skull lying close to the bed of nettles. He detested slugs and tried to squash the thing with his right paw but it used the skull as a kind of shell. He found other bones – picked clean, all mink scent gone. They lay scattered between the river's edge and the den behind the tailrace grid. Greyhood sniffed at them but could not know Broom.

After the little fat man had damaged the roof of the den, couch grass and Friesians' hooves closed the tears and sealed them tight. Then Oak's youngest daughter had come from Strathall and made the hole a den again. She worked very hard and wasted herself. Sloe and her daughter Whin had found easier things to do, for Whin used Fall's den in the Holly Planting and Sloe returned to her old den near the Bridge Hole pool. But Broom, still working when December began, died of hunger and cold the night before the redwings came.

Now, on the afternoon of the twelfth day of December, Greyhood crept through the grid into the den's entrance and he knew where he was going. Halfway along the tunnel he felt the air of a she-mink and knew Broom. He went on and came to the den proper and saw dead grass for a bed. He peered and sniffed at it and touched it with his right paw. Broom had gone and left the place empty.

Just as darkness was falling he moved through the grid and hurried away, past the ash tree over the den and into the Long Meadow. He was hungry and wanted fur and feathers for a couch.

All that evening Greyhood explored the meadow and killed two rabbits and three mice. He ate the mice but dragged the rabbits back to the den. By eight o'clock in the morning, when first light came and rime told of the coming of winter, he was asleep beside McCourt's Stream once again.

For the next week Greyhood hunted and killed through a frosty mist and searched familiar places: the Sandpit, the Brae-field, the Long Meadow and the woodland beyond the scrubby bank. Always he found food to bring back to the den where he had made himself a better couch.

During the later gloaming of the twentieth day of December, Greyhood stayed indoors. Midnight would bring the first morning of winter. No matter; he would stay warm and sleep contentedly.

THE FOXES

O N THE twenty-first morning of December a north-easterly wind moved heavy grey clouds up the Faughan and rain and sleet fell. By the afternoon all the rain had turned to sleet and blackbirds, robins and thrushes sheltered under laurel and holly bushes. That evening the sleet went away to Sawel Mountain and the cold sharpened. Soon after midnight, when the shortest day had gone, the wind started again and blew hard; and powdery snow, hurrying all about the place, left as soon as it came. Before first light the wind eased to let thicker snowflakes form. The snow fell all morning. In mid-afternoon the sky cleared and the snow stopped, leaving the Faughan's banks skimmed with white.

At twenty-five minutes to five, when full darkness came, Greyhood stared through the grid at McCourt's left bank. Soon he felt the bank crisp and cold, felt the taller grass and ferns stiff and more jaggy than before, and burned his tongue licking his feet clean. Seconds later he returned to the den and he went straight to bed.

The next day stayed dry and frosty until half-past nine in the evening. Then a south wind brought rain to leave the place green for Christmas Eve; and Greyhood left the den for a while and chased a large doe rat through the nettle-bed. He caught it and was taking her back to the den when a familiar smell made him pause to look at the opening beside the ash tree over the den. There he saw a she-fox. She was standing very still, staring at him, waiting to take his rat away. He dropped it and retreated past Broom's skull into the grey-brown nettles. There he stopped and looked round again, and watched the vixen stooping to lift the rat. And waving a white-tipped tail, she ran through the gap by the ash tree, taking his rat into the night. When he had peered and searched the air long enough to know the coast was clear he hurried home.

The vixen went back to her earth in the woodland beyond the scrubby bank. Just ten months old and spending her first winter alone, she had used the fox-hole since the first of October's gales brought her down to Glenkeen from Lisdillon Hill and she would continue to use it until the end of May.

During the later morning of Christmas Eve a freshet took Broom's skull and bones away, and went away itself an hour before the dawn of Christmas Day.

Many times during the week that followed, Greyhood saw the she-fox with the white-tipped tail and always ran out of her way. Then in the first afternoon of the New Year, while watching boundary fighting between two robins at the woodland's edge, his heart all but doubled its beat when the vixen strolled past him to hunt the scrubby bank. Truly vulpine from fang to white-tipped brush, she had used the breeze to arrive the way she did and Greyhood could only stand and watch her passing by. With the air against her, he had completely missed her coming. But without a rat or any other food to take away from him, she was not interested in Greyhood. No matter; at all times he would be very wary of her, for she had taken his rat and then caught him unawares.

Every day during the first week of January, he watched robins and listened to their songs. He watched them threaten each other, with soft bills pointing at the sky and bright breasts and throats fully exposed. Facing each other, only a foot apart, he watched them slowly sway from side to side before jumping forward to attack. Then one would hurry away.

Since the Fruit Moon's wane, cock and hen robins had staked out their own territories again. Throughout December many had paired off together and by the end of January many other pairs would form. All of them showing orange-red breasts, they joined and shared their territories in readiness for the season ahead. Soon the time for proper courtship would come with a fight, and a gift; and then, after Saint Patrick's Day, a new home for the young. But now Greyhood watched them chasing each other all about the place and listened to their songs.

Except for the willows with a few yellow leaves still clinging on, and the holly and other evergreens, all the bushes and trees of the Faughan looked idle and naked. Yet much was happening. The different willows were showing growth buds on twigs of different colours: the white willow with brown twigs showed tiny buds covered with white silky hairs; the golden to brownish-green

121

twigs of the crack willow carried bronze-coloured buds with long tapering points and the goat willow, with tiny growths on green or red or purple twigs, showed shiny brown catkin buds as well.

Alongside the willows the alders were busy too, showing last year's fruits ready to fall and new male and female catkins together. The male catkins, elongated and offering a purple tinge, were hard to miss. The females – tiny round black-brown fruits – were hard to see. Last year's fruits, obvious and hopeful, woody and cone-like and opening wide to deliver themselves, would use the Faughan to carry their seeds to low muddy banks to germinate and grow.

Behind the willows and alders, the hairy twigs of hazel held green or reddish buds, and catkins, all waiting to expand. The birches, with long thin whippy twigs, had growth buds and catkins too. And the thorn bushes, sycamores, elms and all the other bushes and trees awaited the unfolding of another spring.

On the ninth day of January, just before noon, Greyhood felt fish-smells through the smells of rats and became very hungry. From the nettle-bed he watched four rats at a salmon at the river's edge. The salmon lay on dry gravel and sand and made the rats look small. Greyhood knew the kind of the great fish and expected it to leap away, but nothing happened. He waited awhile and closely watched the rats at their carryings-on. Then he left the nettle-bed and saw the rats looking at him, all of them with heads held high, and he heard them saying things to each other. They seemed angry and sat on hunkers daring him to come but, when he ran straight at them, they fled.

Beside the abandoned fish, with ears and eyes wide open, Greyhood waited for the rats to return with more of their kind, but they stayed away. So he ate the cock kelt's head and dragged the fish towards the den. Five minutes later, halfway along McCourt's sandy bank, he paused awhile to rest. Then he moved the fish up the bank and had to pull hard to get the thing through the grid before the den.

Later that same afternoon, after eating the kelt's belly bare and empty, he returned to search beyond the nettle patch. There he hoped to find another fish but found nothing.

Many times during the week that followed, Greyhood returned

122

to the throat of McCourt's to find other salmon but found none. But he was not always hungry, for rabbits were easily caught in the Long Meadow and the woodland beyond the scrubby bank, and he kept a good supply of fresh meat against the back wall of the den. Usually he stayed about the river's left bank for there was no need to go any other place. Seldom was he tempted to swim to the Faughan's far bank. Most times he slept dry, and slept more and more with every new day.

One sunny afternoon, about thirty yards beyond the nettle-bed and close to the river's edge, a warm sweet smell led him to sniff at heliotropes. That same afternoon, after climbing over mossy hummocks, he found a patch of flowering snowdrops near the Berryburn Bridge. And later he watched a score of linnets, all together, some with grey heads and auburn breasts, causing the flowers on gorse to tremble.

Many times during the second week of January, he heard foxes barking and screaming in the woodland beyond the scrubby bank. Soon the vixen from Lisdillon Hill would carry young and he would see them with their parents on Easter Day.

Over the weekend the air grew colder and the first night of January's third week showed ten thousand stars, silent and watchful, blinking back at anything that looked skyward. Soon after sunrise a new dampness crept into the air and, as the morning and afternoon wore on, the sun paled and then grew hazy. At ten minutes past three o'clock, when hail came with a fresh north-easterly wind, the sun disappeared and stayed away. That evening the wind became light but heavy clouds moved over Slievebuck and snow began falling on the Faughan's middle reaches. It fell thick and heavy and at an angle across the valley, slanting away from the entrance to the den in the sloping left bank of McCourt's.

When the snow came Greyhood ran all the way home from the scrubby bank and went straight to bed.

It fell off and on for seven hours, and heightened the figure, form and shape of every still thing in every silent space and left the place all black-and-white. In the early morning the sky cleared to let the stars and moon see frost veneering all the damp things with ice and watch the willows' last leaves letting go.

123

The next day the snow stayed away and an hour of sunshine warmed the taller grasses. But a dry wind from the east and a thickening haze kept the ice without cracks and the snow where it lay. The wind cut through the breasts of many linnets and others of their kind, and took their breath away. And magpies and greyback crows ate tiny birds all day. That night the frost stayed and drifting fog rimed the grasses and other rescued plants. It was a very cold night.

All the while Greyhood had remained indoors and slept long and sound, only stirring when the drumming of pouring rain and the roar of the Faughan in spate woke him four days later. And even then he closed his eyes and fell asleep again, and slept until that evening.

Two days before, with the coming of a wind from the south-west, the rimed plants had begun weeping, ice started to crack and the snow turned soft. The snow slid from all the upright and sloping things but stayed where it lay on flat ground. Then a stronger air moved clouds from the Atlantic and, after crossing Slievekirk, their drizzle turned the snow to slush. The drizzle, snow-water, and melting ice made the Faughan colder and cock kelts, wearing patches of fungus, became much weaker than before. But worse was to follow with the coming of more drizzle and then heavy rain. The river grew much stronger and started washing the kelts away. All the snow and ice had gone and the birds were safe from the cold once more but the cock kelts of Leg na gun were being swept away, and their hens watched them going.

At eight o'clock in the evening of January's fourth Sunday, Greyhood ventured out again and he stood awhile to watch McCourt's in spate. The stream was three feet higher than usual but was beginning to fine down. The night was starless and the air felt damp for a light wind from the south-west was easing clouds across the valley. But the air was warmer than before and the clouds were far too high to bring rain.

He gathered his wits and climbed the bank to run with the breeze into the Long Meadow. Hurrying round the ash, leaving brown bracken and a tussock of grass, he found fresh padding leading into the centre of the meadow. He followed the line and

124

saw a rabbit running into a patch of dead thistles. He stopped. The breeze would carry his air into the thistles. So he hastened away in the direction of the scrubby bank. Thirty yards later, moving all the while, he veered left and ran just as far again towards the upper end of the meadow. Beyond the centre of the meadow he turned left to see the thistle patch before his view of the river, and stopped. Now facing the breeze he could smell a she-rabbit and knew that his own smell would stay away from her face. Her thickening smell took him slowly and silently towards the thistles, and a big dog fox, peering from a gap in gorse on the scrubby bank, watched him all the way.

In her hidy-hole the pregnant doe felt safe and was licking her belly when Greyhood killed her. He killed her with one bite and the big dog fox stood and watched her die.

Now the fox left the scrubby bank and ran into the meadow. Twenty-five yards from the thistles, running across the breeze, he let his feet make noises. He wanted to chase the fitch away but he would not use his voice in open ground. He had no fear of any mink, not even the strange grey thing in the patch of thistles, but he preferred not to suffer the annoyance of a single scratch for a rabbit. He put down his feet with all his might and he slowed his pace.

Greyhood was eating the breast of the doe when sounds of padded grass and stubble made him turn his head to see the fox. He saw a big fiery-brown dog, with puffed-out cheeks and hanging tongue, coming his way to cause trouble. And almost instantly, Greyhood turned away as fast as he could and left the thistles. He galloped down the meadow and through the gap by the ash tree, and the fox watched him go.

Within two minutes, while the fox was carrying the doe through the scrubby bank, Greyhood was lying on his couch listening to McCourt's Stream. Soon after, he heard foxes barking and screaming in the woodland beyond the Long Meadow and dozed off and on for the rest of the night.

The following evening Greyhood returned to the meadow and saw rabbits in open ground near the scrubby bank. Then he saw the dog fox again and lay down to watch him. Without showing any part of himself, in a thick clump of brown bracken, he watched the fox moving out of the gap in gorse on the scrubby bank. The fox moved slowly, with head and belly and tail half hidden in grass, and moved so slowly that the rabbits who saw him stood their ground. Soon the fox stopped and peered at them from a heavy tussock of withered grass. He waited for the rabbits to forget all about him. He waited in a crouched stance and just stared at them.

Greyhood stayed where he lay in the bracken and watched the rabbits growing careless, and knew the mood of the fox. He lay there for two minutes and then he saw the shape of the fox changing. The fox stood higher with face further forward. A doè, without any sense of fear, had followed padding towards the fox and began to mooch around – three yards away. Still the fox waited. Then Greyhood saw a brown blur of movement and heard a rabbit squealing, and saw other rabbits scampering towards the scrubby bank. Then he saw the fox at the rabbit, lifting the squealing thing into the air and making the squeals stop with a shake of his head.

Greyhood crept out of the bracken and left the meadow to return to McCourt's sandy bank. There he stood looking at the far bank and the stream – twelve inches too high to be easily crossed. He could not use the scrubby bank for he did not like the look of the dog fox and ran instead towards the nettle-bed to pick up the scent of rats.

By the next day the Faughan was its own height again and became a golden amber colour, and Greyhood found a cock kelt where McCourt's sandy bank met the stream. The kelt was dead and had suffered disease. Lying on his back in six inches of water, between the otters' rock and dry sand, the fish had patches of cream-coloured fungi all over his jaws and tail. But apart from sniffing at them awhile after dragging the fish ashore, Greyhood ignored these patches and started hauling his great find up the bank.

THE FERRET

During the first afternoon of February, when drifting fog chilled the air, Greyhood crossed Brolly's Burn and ran the length of the Boat Hole's bank to hunt rabbits. There he saw three men at burrows and he turned away to hurry down-river again.

Two days later, when cold air and fog gathered on the river's right bank, he crept into the Pasture behind the sallies in Cross-ballycormack. He had crept under a wire-and-post fence and then through an old blackberry bramble, arriving at the warren in the downstream end of the Pasture. He hid himself in gorse near a well-used burrow. He sat on hunkers and waited and watched for rabbits, and saw men instead. Three men were standing together about twenty yards from him and only a few paces from the middle of the warren. He heard them talking among themselves and he expected them to go. So he lay on his belly and continued looking on.

Two of the men held purse nets, thirty inches long and wide, with metal rings and pegs attached: nylon nets of two-inch mesh for catching rabbits. Two rings on each net were designed to guide a draw-cord through and the single peg would fasten the net to the ground. The third man held a closed ferret bag and a strong iron bar. The bag had a polecat ferret inside – all creamy white with pink eyes. The ferret would be sent into one of the warren's holes and rabbits would try to bolt out the others. But heavy stones would be used to block most of the exits, and the nets spread over any others. And any bolting rabbit would draw the net tight and end up in a bag.

Greyhood stayed where he lay in his hidy-hole in gorse and waited for the men to go. But when they started to walk he sat upright for one of them was coming his way. With eyes searching for a way to escape, he looked all around and then quickly crept into the burrow nearby. Just inside the roomy corridor of rabbit-air he stopped, for light through another hole came dangerously close. He lay in a kind of excited daze and was nearly asleep when his underparts trembled and drumming sounds filled his head. The trembling grew greater and the drumming loudened, then, of a sudden, out of darkness, a bolting rabbit careered towards him and leapt into light through the corridor's roof. The rabbit had gone and he heard a man shouting.

For a time he remained very tense. He stared at the light through the roof and listened to the rabbit struggling and the voices of men. When the sounds went away he settled again to wait another while but started up when the smell of a dog fitch – tainted with man – made his nostrils twitch. The smell drifted towards his face and grew stronger. He stared ahead and felt the ground trembling again, and he kept staring. Then in the dark a grey dimness became a white fitch. Approaching the light through the hole in the roof, he showed pink eyes with centres like blood. Greyhood waited.

He peered at the thing and stayed where he was. He waited for the strange fitch to come nearer. He waited on all fours and stood rigid and looked for signs of rage but found none. The stranger neither bared his teeth nor made strong smells – he showed no signs of rage. Still Greyhood stood his ground and waited, and waited without any fear, for the thing was slow and fat and short underneath, and small enough to take on.

The ferret stopped and stood blinking at Greyhood, and knew danger. He had not met a mink before. He had chased rabbits in tunnels and rats in pits and always they ran away. He would not attempt to chase the thing before him for it wanted him to try. He lifted his head and looked towards the light and worked his nostrils awhile. A second later he went through the hole in the roof, into the Pasture. And Greyhood heard the voices of men and cocked his ears to listen but when the voices grew faint he lay on his belly and rested.

As he lay there, the light through the corridor's roof faded. The sun was behind thick fog on Slievekirk and daylight was going. After a short sleep he left the burrow and crept under the wire-and-post fence to hurry downriver in the direction of Brolly's Burn. The air was very cold. A whisper of wind moved heavy fog across the river from Lisdillon Hill and the ground was so chilled that his belly tingled. He ran along the Boat Hole's bank and saw a buck rat leaving the river and disappearing into the dark spill-over

128

cut in the far side. Daylight had gone.

He crossed Brolly's Burn and disturbed a moorhen in the Sand-pit and watched her rushing towards marshy cover. She gave a loud 'kr-r-rk' and half ran, half flew, on green legs showing a glimpse of white undertail. A short while later Greyhood caught her in the damp ditch alongside the Brae-field. He took her across McCourt's and placed her against the den's back wall. He looked at her awhile and then ate her head, leaving only a bright-red-and-yellow bill on a string of throat flesh. The rest of her, he left alone. He was tired but knew by the air that a cold time was coming. He would need more food.

So he left the den again and ran into the Long Meadow. He remembered the dog fox but went on and caught three rabbits before midnight came and, all the while, the fox stayed away. Soon, tired and very cold, he dragged and pushed his third rabbit behind the den's couch and fell fast asleep.

When he awoke at dusk he ate the moorhen and kept her feathers for the couch. Then, after moving through the grid, he stood and looked about him and saw new banks and trees through a grey mist.

During his sleep the fog had thickened and lingered on, making feathery crystals of frost and every nettle, and any other still and slim thing it touched, white all over and coral-like. Tree branch-lets and twigs and all their buds had the same whiteness and every trunk showed its own colour through a seal of glassy hoar. The meadows and any open places were hard and firm and their grubs and worms were left alone. All the birds left the fields and lap-wings left the valley of the Faughan altogether. Sparrows in farmyards were joined by buntings, pied wagtails and flocks of finches. Pheasants stayed in copses and about the edges of wood-land. Redwings, fieldfares and snipe moved into hedges, and robins, thrushes, blackbirds, wrens and tits kept inside thickets. Only the bottoms of holly and laurel bushes, thickets of bramble and gorse, and hedges sheltering by drystone walls kept soft and open and offered food. The damp corners of fields were hard, reeds and grasses stuck together, and every feed-in trickle had stopped before it reached the river. Only the river itself ran free – especially in its middle – for slow edges and eddies, and pebbles and rocks half submerged in separated shallows were fastened together in ice.

For two minutes Greyhood stood and looked about him and then went back indoors and added the moorhen's feathers to his bed. He stayed there for a week of nights and days and slept.

Then during the eleventh morning of February, the wind went round from the north-east to the west and the air grew warmer. By mid-afternoon clouds from the Atlantic filled the sky and, within an hour, heavy rain fell over the valley and all the hoar frost went away. Quite suddenly the air had become mild and the valley grew soft and damp again and, except for the lapwings who had left altogether, the birds ignored the rain and returned to the meadows. But many birds had not survived.

Later in the evening, when the rain had stopped, Greyhood left the den. He was hungry and alert and sought fresh food. Beyond the nettle-bed he found a dead blackbird with an orange bill and ate him. Soon he was splashing his way across the cricket pitch before the Berryburn and found a black-headed reed bunting and he ate him as well. He found another cock blackbird before the morning came and killed a sow rat to take back to the den.

In the week that followed, the moon turned full and the air became even softer along the valley of the Faughan. The days grew longer too and rats and rabbits were born. And feeling more lonely than before, Greyhood travelled downriver as far as the Beech Wood. There he watched badgers changing their bedding and saw a mallard fixing a nest in a willow's low branches overhanging the Deep-end Craig. Every night, arriving at the edge of the drain before the Daisy Field, he looked towards Fall's den in the Holly Planting, but always turned away. Every morning, a few minutes before sunrise, he was home again in the left bank of McCourt's Stream.

When another week had passed, the hazels let their lambs' tails hang down and the redwings and fieldfares started flying away. February was all but gone and two hours more of the light of day had returned, and many backboned things grew excited in the light and minks were getting ready to meet again. Every hour brought more of a strange new feeling of excitement and, for Greyhood and many others as well, food-seeking and eating grew far less important than before.

In the early dusk of February's extra day, when a cock king-fisher flew upriver through the air of McCourt's Stream and an Irish dipper with a wadge of moss in her beak flew the same way, Greyhood left home to search the Holly Planting.

BAST THE CAT

AFTER CROSSING McCourt's Stream, Greyhood kept beside the river, close to cover, for the sky was broken and badgers were out and about. He did not hurry. Past the Beech Wood he saw the mallard nest at the tail of the Deep-end Craig but moved on. At the edge of the drain into the Bleach-green Dam he stopped to sniff the air and looked around. The river was quiet and the air almost still but the sky grew too bright at times. Turning his head, he sensed neither friend nor foe. But he remained by the drain until the moon would go away. On the other side of the drain was the Daisy Field and in the far side of the Daisy Field stood the dark shape of the Holly Planting. He looked in the direction of Fall's den and remembered it well. Then under a bank of cloud he started making his way across the field. And following a slight breeze through the nearest holly trees, he met Whin of Strathall.

The previous autumn, ten weeks after Fall's death, Whin had left Strathall and moved into the den beneath the holly trees. Larger than Broom and more independent, she was the first of Oak's daughters to leave the Bridge Hole pool and killed a she-stoat from Kilcargay to take Fall's den. Since then she had killed other stoats to keep a home for herself and now she desired the company of her own kind.

A minute after sensing a mink coming her way, she recognised Greyhood and stood fidgety. Now, two yards from him, she stood moving her rump and shaking her tail.

Greyhood, watching her and knowing her without bothering to let on, saw her turn and felt his nostrils flare. Soon his face grew warm and tight. He was confused and felt a strange anger grow. His spring knocked her down and took her by surprise. And then, after returning her touches, he left her alone.

Three hours before March knew daylight, Greyhood left the Holly Planting. And just as the sun was rising, he pushed a half-eaten rat against the back wall of the den and fell fast asleep.

At nightfall he moved slowly into the Long Meadow and stopped to search the air. The noises of foxes came from the scrubby bank. It was a mild night with a gentle downstream breeze bringing clouds all the way from Sawel and carrying rat-smells and bird-smells from the Berryburn. So, turning left, he ran towards the upstream end of the meadow. Soon he slipped through a hedge of hawthorns and then crossed the cricket pitch before the burn. He was hungry and thirsty.

At the burn he spent some time lapping up water and then lifted his head to look around. He remained where he was and, save for moving his head and parts of his face, he stood still. Then he lifted his face sharply, as high as he could and turning his head to meet a new scent, he found himself staring at the mill. Now, keeping his body very still, he continued to stare at the mill, letting the smell fill his head, and he wondered about its owner.

The smell was very strange. It was almost like the air from old summer's flowering-currant bush or the tall benweed in bloom or the damp brown grass in the dispenser, but it was an animal's smell. It was blood-warm and fur-soft, and coming and going, but altogether sharp. It was not the smell of a cousin – of a musky fitch of any kind. Without any oil, it was not the smell of a fish. It was not the turnip-smell of a fox; the woody smell of the great black dog; the sour smell of a hedgehog or the sweet smell of a long-tailed mouse. Greyhood had never met such a smell. It was not the smell of any man or cow or sheep or furry thing he knew, or bird or fish, or any kind of plant. It was very strange.

He continued sniffing the air and staring at the old mill. He disliked the air for his eyes were watering and he felt uneasy. No matter; he crossed the burn and moved very slowly into the mill's tailrace.

The smell belonged to a huge tom cat called Bast, an Abyssinian, a descendant of the sacred family of Bubastis of ancient Egypt. Grey-brown in coat with hazel eyes, lithe and muscular with slender legs, Bast lay curled in the Berryburn Mill. Thirty-six inches long and fifteen pounds strong, with chin resting on ten-inch tail, he lay half asleep and dangerous.

Born three years before, in a barn in the place called Kinculbrack, just outside Claudy village, Bast had grown half-wild and very bad-tempered. For two years he had fed on rats and wild birds, and rabbit heads, and then started taking domestic fowl and attacking other pets like himself. In the early afternoon of the fifteenth day of February he seriously injured a Yorkshire terrier. And later that afternoon he was taken downriver and abandoned in Legaghory's Chestnut Glen. Now a fortnight later, after hunting Gosheden, Knockbrack and the length of Ardkill, he had arrived at the old mill before the Berryburn and was resting on a tussock of yellow-brown grass in one of the mill's far corners. And, all the while, bolt upright in the opposite corner, on the mill's highest ledge, the barn owl watched him.

Greyhood followed the line of Bast's scent and moved along the old tailrace to reach the mill's nearest wall. After climbing out of the trench and creeping round the corner of the wall, he peered through the entrance into darkness and saw and heard a most frightening thing. Bast, waiting with ears lying level and body arched high, let out a yowl and leapt through the air. Greyhood turned and ran for his life. He ran all the way to the Faughan's edge and jumped from six feet of bank into the Boat Hole pool. He charged up the far bank and stopped and looked around. He looked across at the bank before the mill but saw nothing. Then he hurried downriver towards Brolly's Burn.

Angry, but not wanting to exert himself for dry stringy meat, Bast stood in the mill's doorway and watched the fitch go. There he stood awhile and relaxed and let his ears lift high, and heard a rustle of feathers from behind and somewhere above. Pretending not to hear anything of the kind, he moved to the mouth of a hole near his feet and lowered his head to listen to the voices of rats. Then very quickly, he lifted his head and saw a she-owl staring back. Two hours later, when a noisy wind came, he left the mill and let the owl see him go. Soon after, he crept through a gap in the building's torn roof and took the white owl unawares. She blinked once and was halfway through a second, and died before she could snap her bill – let alone fly.

THE SHE-MINK DUN

ALL THAT remaining night and during every night of the first week of March, Greyhood hunted the far bank downstream of Brolly's Burn. He had seen and heard a most fearsome enemy, fiercer than any he had met before, and he disliked the smell of the thing. For that full week he stayed away from the stretch upstream of the Berryburn but, an hour after midnight had started the eighth day of March, he hurried along the right bank to find Sloe of Strathall. He followed her into her den beside the Bridge Hole pool and spent that day and three more with her. At night, when out and about, they hunted the Wood of Strathall and the Chestnut Glen and sometimes Humpy Meadow. At all times they stayed together. Then during the early dusk of the twelfth day of March, Greyhood continued upriver alone to find a bitch in Tamneymore.

While he was hurrying with a strong breeze along the right bank of the pool called Jeannie Lyons, another mink moved downriver from the Ness Burn. After crossing the burn and smelling Greyhood in the upstream air, the mink had moved slowly along the bank to meet him and now stood inside a holly tree to watch him coming.

The elder brother of Thorn of Tamneymore, this mink was a killer of dogs of his own kind and his name was Garm. The colour of charcoal, broader than Thorn and just as tall, he was a year older than Greyhood and looked twice as strong. About six and a half inches high, and twenty-seven inches long, he was fierce and very powerful and his vast territory stretched from Strathall to two miles beyond the Red Berry Wood – nearly three miles altogether. During the first ten days of March he had mated upstream of Gosheden Bridge, then in the early gloaming of the twelfth day, he moved downriver to find Sloe of Strathall. Now he was going to meet another dog instead. And when a grey mink came into view, Garm left the holly tree to kill him.

Following the breeze and hoping to find signs of a bitch, Greyhood had paused to examine old scats but found nothing else. Then, when a shadow left a holly tree about thirty yards ahead, he moved round a stump of beech and saw a big dog mink and expected trouble. Greyhood stood very still and waited to do battle.

He watched Garm coming all the way and saw his teeth and wild eyes and hairs bristling, and was out of reach by less than two yards when Garm left the ground. Immediately, Greyhood moved to the right to let him pass and then twisted round to take him from behind. But he need not have bothered for Garm lay dead: met by the stump of beech, his skull was badly broken and his face and chest were caved in. Greyhood looked at him awhile and left him for others to take.

That night the river ran quiet and baby salmon wriggled free. More than a month before – less than two months after cock fish had sprayed their redds – tiny black specks had peered through the walls of eggs. Since then, by feeding on yolk, the eyed ova had developed into lively embryonic things. Now the tiny alevins were moving into the gravel of the outside world to rest awhile. Four days from now, scaleless and colourless and sensitive to light, they would seek the darker places of the streams and finish off their sacs of yolk before Easter Day. Then, as fry, they would begin to show their true colours and fend for themselves. Many would be killed: only three out of every hundred would live to be called parrs and, between hatching free and growing into silvery smolts, only a few would survive. Many of them would be eaten, others would just die.

During the remaining night, without finding any signs of any bitch, Greyhood searched the right bank before Gosheden Bridge. And then, half an hour after first light, while a cock buzzard made a roller-coaster flight over Strathall, he crossed to the Faughan's left bank. Soon he carried a young buck rabbit into the empty rat-pit in the upper end of Humpy Meadow, ate him, and slept soundly until the evening.

Nearly a mile downstream of Humpy Meadow, in the Barley Field in Ardkill, another mink was sleeping. Lying in the disused rabbit-stab beneath the female holly tree, she had been living there since late October. She lay curled on rabbit fur, her chin resting on bushy tail with tiny front paws tucked under, and she slept contentedly. A daughter of Thorn, but dark brown and marked like most of the Faughan's other minks, her name was Dun.

Since crossing the river from Tamneymore, a week after her father's death, Dun had experienced many frights: shots fired from the gun of a little fat man below Gosheden Bridge; a great black dog near the Bridge Hole pool; coming face to face with a sow badger in the Dungeon Glen and, in more recent times, watching a huge cat-thing prowling the bank of the Barley Field. No matter; she remained unharmed and slept contentedly.

That evening, just as darkness was falling, while leaving the den under the holly tree and looking towards the upstream end of the field, she saw a big dog mink coming her way. She stopped and waited and grew excited.

An hour before, Greyhood had left the rat-pit in Humpy Meadow, moved through the Chestnut Glen and crossed the narrow burn between Legaghory and Gosheden. After the burn, where the river leaves the Bridge Hole to hurry as streams, Greyhood followed the left bank and ran through the Dungeon Glen to enter Knockbrack. Soon after, he crossed the Horsey Burn and crept into the Barley Field. There he dallied no more for a bitch stood waiting.

As Greyhood ran over stubble, disturbing birds of different kinds, he saw the she-mink looking at him and felt his excitement grow. Still she stood, without a fidget, as though she had known him all her days. He ran on and was less than three yards away when she stooped to crouch and stare. Soon, without taking her eyes off Greyhood, she lay on her belly. In his younger days he had seen his mother do the same thing with Oak – she had made no effort to run away. He stopped and looked at Dun and stayed still.

For seconds neither moved. Then Greyhood crept slowly forward, stopped again and lowered his face. Now, just under a yard away, his muzzle was touching the ground and his eyes were level with the black eyes of the bitch. And when she opened her mouth as if to yawn but purred and started to roll away, he moved forward and made her stay.

Afterwards they hunted the Barley Field and along the Quiet Glade, and then when daylight came they crept into the den beneath the holly tree and slept.

In the third week of March, when cub foxes opened their eyes for the very first time, Greyhood and Dun hunted and played together and wandered upstream. On the eve of Saint Patrick's Day, when a strong breeze brought rain, they watched pipistrelles near the Horsey Burn. That same evening they saw a grey heron standing at the March Hole and watched a dog otter making bubbles in the belly of Leg na gun. The following day, in the early gloaming, they saw the great black dog hurrying after a grey-haired man heading downriver towards the Ardkill Dam. They saw hen kelts tailing downstream in twelve inches of fresh water and saw dippers and grey wagtails and kingfishers too. They watched rooks, with sticks in their mouths, flying towards the Beech Wood. Usually by day they rested together in the Barley Field's den under the female holly tree. But sometimes Dun would chase Greyhood away and then he would use the stab-cum-den in the Green Meadow. Always he returned to stay with her at night.

When the next week brought spring and sounds of wind and hail and rain, spent brownies and sea trout returned to the swollen river after dallying awhile in their spawning burns. Noisy frogs mated in the Sandpit and three otters were born in the holt in the left bank of Leg na gun. Badgers had young in the Beech Wood and Dungeon Glen; leverets were born on Gosheden Hill; red squirrels were on family duties through the Wood of Strathall; rabbits and rats and mice were nursing too and quiet birds were busy everywhere. Along the river the catkins of hazel and willow were easily seen and new stems and leaves of various grasses and flowering plants were making their presence felt. Buckler-ferns were getting ready to uncoil and the flowers of elms gave Strathall a reddish-purple hue. And, all the while, Greyhood hunted and played and sometimes slept with Dun.

As March knew more heat and light and the heavy breezes went away, the Faughan's wild things grew. Most of the river's mammals were feeding young. Many birds were sitting on eggs and fish fry were coming on. Elvers had arrived from the sea while kelts were going out. Much was happening during the last week of March and, most noticeable of all, new plants were growing everywhere. On the banks white patches of anemone and beds of yellow celandine began to show. The white flowers of blackthorn thorn gave out their smell and the scent of sweet violet could be felt as well. The flowers of gorse and primroses were brightening scrubby banks and, in the corners of meadows, speedwells and horsetails, woodrush and red dead-nettles grew. Wood spurge grew near ground ivy with violet flowers lipped with purple spots. And, throughout woods, a few snowdrops lingered and under the oaks the leaves of bluebells had appeared. Soon the wood sorrel and dog violet and all the others would come, and the brambles and the bushes and trees would leaf. Before long, about the Faughan's middle reaches and elsewhere along the valley, butterflies and bees and other organisms would appear – and fishermen too. And once more the Faughan would run its course to welcome salmon and trout returning from the sea.

During the second night of April, after leaving the Barley Field and finding plenty to eat through the upper end of the Green Meadow, Greyhood and Dun went to the Boat Hole to bathe and play. When they arrived the pool was dark and quiet for the river ran low and a black cloud had come with an easy breeze over Slievekirk. But they disturbed a hen kelt near the mouth of Madam's Burn and the pool grew very noisy. Chasing the fish down and across the pool, they made her jump all about the place and the commotion could be heard a hundred yards away.

The hen fish running with the river, spending all her energy and losing more by leaping through the air, crossed the Faughan to lie beside the spill-over cut from the old layde to the mill. And when teeth like hooks dug into her tail-wrist and side and she tried to leap away from the pains, her efforts to escape were heard by the cat called Bast.

He heard the splashing from the other side of the mill where he was hunting and turned round and began to run. He sped into the spill-over cut and, within seconds, he appeared on the bank of the Boat Hole pool. There he saw two minks hauling at a great fish and now, a moment later, he watched the minks flee.

While pushing and dragging the salmon onto a dry sandy bed and turning their own heads towards a heavy smell from atop the bank, Greyhood and Dun had seen a most fearsome sight. Yellow eyes, staring from a shape which filled the sky, glared at them and they left their fish and swam across the pool at their fastest speed. Greyhood went first, then, climbing the far bank and glancing over their right shoulders, they saw Bast dropping to the sandy bed to take their fish. Soon after, upstream of the Pullens, they crossed the Faughan again and returned to the Barley Field beyond Leg na gun.

DARKNESS

For several nights more Greyhood stayed with Dun and they hunted both sides of the river from the Glen of the Guns to Leg na gun. They stayed well away from the Boat Hole. Then on the evening of Easter Day, when Dun pretended to chase him away again, Greyhood moved downriver to hunt the Long Meadow. He wanted to be alone but Bast the cat followed him all the way.

Just before sunset a family of foxes came out to play and a grey-haired man with a black dog lay inside a laurel bush to watch them.

They were the family of the vixen who came from Lisdillon Hill – the vixen with the white-tipped tail who had taken Greyhood's rat away. And her mate was the fox who had chased Greyhood from the thistle patch. Mother and father with four cubs, all fiery-brown, they played near their earth under gorse on the woodland side of the scrubby bank. Now the cubs, three dogs and a bitch, born just over a month before, jumped up to reach their parents' mouths.

There was no breeze from any direction that evening and the woodland's trees, with their leaves still closed, were letting all the light get through. The dog fox, golden red beneath Slievekirk's sun, began chasing his tail. And downstream, sixty yards away, the man and dog looked on.

While his master lay watching the foxes and he crouched on mulch and looked around, something else was seen by the dog, and his body stiffened. Suddenly he sat upright, growling, and as he stared past the foxes his back-hairs tightened.

The man followed the dog's stare through the scrubby bank and saw two animals a good distance away. Then, as they came closer he saw a mink and a cat. The mink was approaching the scrubby bank, and not far behind the cat was following it. Settling the flustered dog, the man watched Greyhood and Bast the cat coming their way.

At the scrubby bank Greyhood, hearing noises in the wood nearby, crept close to the gap in gorse and saw foxes staring at him. He jumped into a clump of buckler-ferns, where rabbits sometimes lay, and stayed there. He lay as still as could be, peering ahead with nostrils and ears held high, not knowing that Bast was coming the other way.

From the laurel bush the man and dog watched the foxes running to earth and the cat approaching the buckler-ferns where the grey mink lay. When the sun moved down behind Slievekirk and the foxes had gone to earth they left the laurel bush to see what the cat would do.

Greyhood had been hiding in the ferns for a full minute when Bast's smell made his head jerk round. Then, when a darkness filled the sky, he heard a fearful purr-cum-snarl and felt his nose being ripped away. He tried to roll sideways and he tried his best to fight but he could only scream as burning feelings pinned him where he lay. And as great claws pierced his neck making the rest of him go numb, he heard the voice of a man shout out; then he knew no more.

ABOUT WILD MINKS

Greyhood was a wild American mink (*Mustela vison*), a member of the family Mustelidae – the weasel family. The badger, otter and stoat are members of this family. Almost half of the wild carnivorous mammals in Europe are musteline. The American mink is our most recent member.

Originally brought to western Europe in the late 1920s, this animal was control-bred for its rich fur. During World War II, the fur trade declined and minks escaped from captivity. In the late 1950s and early 1960s the trade picked up but, within ten years, it dwindled again and more minks escaped into the wild. Consequently, today's increase in the feral mink population dates from the mid-1970s. They thrive along the river banks of Britain and Ireland, being the most abundant carnivore in many areas.

Nearly all of these wild minks have reverted to the natural coloration of their forebears. The fur of most of them is the colour of burnt toast with a white patch on the lower lip and chin, and a few white marks on the breast and belly. However, continuous topping-up of the feral population gives rise to a variety of colours. Some appear totally black while others are heavily marked. But the prized grey and pale brown coats, produced by controlled breeding, are seldom seen in the wild. Greyhood was exceptional.

The American mink is an arrogant little animal. Normally quiet and purring, when cornered – or caged – it will emit a strong musky smell and scream in a scolding fashion as a last-ditch effort to defend itself. Along the river bank it can make a den among rocks, in holes in trees, in unused pipes or in the burrows of other animals. A female has a short-range territory. A male will travel long distances and mate with several females as he moves through their territories. They usually mate in February through March and delayed implantation extends the 30-day gestation to 39–76 days. The single litter of five or six kits are mature in their first year and breed the following spring. The average mature male, 60 cm long, including a 16–17 cm tail, is twice the size of the female.

The American mink can run quickly and catch a rat, leap

suddenly and take a moorhen, search small burrows and kill a stoat, climb high bushes and rob a nest, fish for fluke and other slow fishes and swim strongly with a cub rabbit in its mouth. It seems to prefer hunting from mid-evening through the night but a female with hungry kits will also be seen during the day.

These versatile and highly skilled predators are much maligned. They are accused of breeding like rats, attacking pets, killing poultry and lambs, and threatening the numbers of available native species. These kinds of accusations have caused researchers to prove the animal's innocence rather than its guilt. Eight years of observing their behaviour for *Greyhood* revealed that, in any year, wild minks have one litter of five or six kits, most of which die before reaching maturity. Minks avoid cats and dogs. They do not kill lambs. Like badgers and stoats, they will slaughter hens, and pheasants in pens, but they can survive successfully along quiet stretches of river without going anywhere near captive or domestic stock.

In rivers and streams they compete with otters for eels, slow fishes and diseased trout and salmon. The otters are better fishers. Moorhens, mallard and rats disappear for awhile but they soon return. Once minks colonise an area, they protect their own territories and control their own numbers. Trapping programmes fail since they only make territories available to other wandering minks. They are wild carnivores, determined to survive. And they soon learn not to kill too much – or store too much. There is no need: food is plentiful and better fresh.

The American mink is here to stay. And this is the most remarkable thing of all. For it is the first wild carnivorous mammal from another clime to make itself at home in these islands.

GLOSSARY

alevin	newly hatched salmon or trout
alulae	set of three or four quill-like feathers growing at the small joint in the middle of a bird's wing; bastard wing
backwatering	halting forward movement by reverse action of the wings
brae-field	sloping field
carry steps	triangular-shaped steps built on to the face of a weir for running fish
cleik	to seize firmly or suddenly with a gaff or large hook
dun	immature adult mayfly
feral	existing in a wild state, especially after being domestic or cultivated
fitch	belonging to the weasel family – mink, stoat, badger, otter etc.
founds	foundations
freshet	a *small* flood caused by heavy rains or melted snow
glade	sheltered stretch of slow-moving river
hob	shelf of rock or collapsed bank between normal level of river and top of bank
holt	otters' den
hurry	stretch of fast-flowing river
kelt	salmon or sea trout that has spawned and is weak and spent through loss of energy and food reserves
knob	lump on tree trunk
krill	small shimp-like marine crustacean
kype	hook of gristle projecting upwards at tip of lower jaw of a male salmon
layde	trench or ditch with gate or gates for holding back or controlling the water of a millrace
lie	lodge where salmon rest and shelter from the full force of the current
millrace	current of water that turns a millwheel
mulch	half-rotten vegetable matter
parr	name given to young trout or salmon when pigment cells begin to develop in the skin
plantain	broad-leaved plants
picker	immature sea trout at stage when it migrates from brackish water of estuary to sea
ream	arrow-like ripple pushed by a water-rat or mink

redd	nest made by salmon or trout in which to spawn
roller-coaster	flight used by buzzards during courtship
scaldy	baby animal lacking hair, feathers or other natural covering
sallies	willows
scat	animal dropping
smolt	young salmon or trout at the stage when it migrates from fresh water to estuary
spill-over cut	narrow trench or ditch that carries excess water away from a millrace
spoor	track of an animal
spraint	otter droppings
stab	short blind burrow where a rabbit delivers and nurses her cubs
stab-cum-den	rabbit-stab used by minks
tail	lower end of pool or part of stream
tailrace	channel that carries water away from waterwheel or turbine
thole	to suffer, bear, put up with

NOTES ON PLACE NAMES

Ardkill	*Ardchoill:* high woodland
Ardmore	*Ard Mór:* great height
Ballynameen	*Baile na Míne:* townland of the green mountain pasture
Ballyshasky	*Baile Seascaigh:* barren townland
Campsie	*Camsán:* a meandering stretch of river
Chestnut Glen	In this book, a part of the private property known as Oaks' Lodge
Claudy	*Cláideach:* mountain torrent
Cloghornagh	*Clochar an Átha:* stony ridge of the ford
Crossballycormack	*Cros Bhaile Chormaic:* cross of Cormac's townland
Deep-end Craig	The deep end of the fishing pool called the Craig Hole
Derry	*Doire:* oak wood
Drumahoe	*Droim na hUamha:* ridge of the cave
Faughan	*Fothain:* sheltered place
Foyle	*An Feabhal:* a mythical personal name, according to tradition from *Feabhail Mic Lodain,* the son of Lodain – one of the *Tuatha Dé Danaan,* who was drowned in the river, and whose body was cast ashore by the waves
Glenkeen	*Gleann Caoin:* gentle glen
Gosheden	*Geosadán:* land abounding in thistles
Humpy Meadow	In this book, a part of the private property known as Oaks' Lodge
Jeannie Lyons	The pool where Jane Lyons drowned
Kilcargay	*Coill Charraigeach:* rocky woodland
Kinculbrack	*Ceann Cúlbhreac:* speckle-backed hilltop
Knockbrack	*Cnoc Breac:* speckled hill
Legaghory	*Log an Choire:* corrie hollow
Leg na gun	*Log na gCon:* hounds' hollow or pool; lie of the hound
Lisdillon	*Lios Uí Dhilghin:* O'Dillon's enclosure
Lismacarol	*Lios Mac Cearrbhaill:* McCarroll's fort
Loughermore	*Luachair Mhór:* great rushy place
March Hole	A fishing pool between the townlands of Strathall and Crossballycormack
Ness	From *eas:* waterfall

Pullens	*Pollán:* small pool
Sawel	*Sabhall:* barn
Slievebuck	*Sliabh Boc:* mountain of the buck
Slievekirk	*Sliabh Circe:* mountain of the grouse or hen
Sperrins	*Speirín:* mountain spur
Strathall	*Srath Aill:* river holm of the cliff or rock
Tamneymore	*Tamhnach Mhór:* large tract of arable land in the mountain
Tyrone	*Tír Eoghain:* the land of Eoghan, one of the three sons of Niall of the Nine Hostages
Wood of Strathall	In this book, the name used for the private property known as The Oaks